THE IRISH TIMES

BOOK

OF

JESUS

REPORTS

XXX-XXXIII AD

PATSY McGARRY

IRISH TIMES BOOKS

First published October 2001 by
Irish Times Books
an imprint of
THE IRISH TIMES

© **THE IRISH TIMES**
and Patsy McGarry

Distribution: **Irish Times Books**
10 – 16 D'Olier Street, Dublin 2, Ireland.
Telephone (01) 6758271
Fax (01) 6718446
email itbooks@irish-times.ie

2 4 6 8 10 9 7 5 3 1

ISBN 0 907011 33 0

Project Director: Brenda McNiff
Administration: Julie Dobson

Designed & Printed
in the Republic of Ireland
by Mahons Printing Works, Dublin

DEDICATION

This collection of Jesus Reports is dedicated to two remarkable women: my mother Teenie McGarry, without whom it would not have been possible, and my first teacher Mrs Molly Forde without whom it would not have happened.

In 1999, when I first mentioned writing these reports, my mother bought no less than four different versions of the New Testament for me. They gave a broad denominational spread to the accounts of Matthew, Mark, Luke, and John, and all four were consulted regularly as the reports were written through the year 2000.

At primary school Mrs Forde taught us the gospel stories, many of which feature in this book and which have remained with me all my life. She was our only teacher then at the small school in Mullen, near Frenchpark, Co Roscommon, which is now closed.

I was with Mrs Forde until I was ten when my family moved to Ballaghaderreen. A deeply Christian woman her impact on me was deep and not least because of an episode at the school when I was about six.

The diocesan examiner came around and asked us various questions about the gospels. All was going well until the priest asked us who was the husband of Elizabeth and father of John (the Baptist). We were stumped until I suddenly remembered, and shouted out "Zachary". Since that day I have been unable to do anything wrong in Mrs Forde's eyes.

Patsy McGarry
October 2001

ACKNOWLEDGEMENTS

I am indebted to many people mostly colleagues in *The Irish Times*. *The Editor* Conor Brady, and the then *News Editor* Niall Kiely; Willy Clingan and John Maher who took over as *News Editor* and *Deputy News Editor*, respectively, while the work was in progress and who were always accommodating in an enterprise which had nothing to do with the *Home News* pages for which I work.

My colleagues on the *Foreign Desk* deserve medals for their patience during the year. They never demurred at the loss of valuable space to this endeavour and were grace itself in helping see it through.

I am indebted to Bernard Harris for his diligence in helping to put the reports into book format and for compiling the lists of scripture references; to Jerome Murphy-O'Connor OP for his kindness in writing the Introduction, to Bernard Treacy OP for his perceptive advice on reading the work; and not least to Brenda McNiff, *General Services Manager*, who together with Julie Dobson, has seen this book through to publication.

CONTENTS

PREFACE

This book is not intended to be either definitive or
exhaustive. Nor, for that matter, is it only directed at the
committed or informed Christian. It is aimed primarily at the
lukewarm, the semi-informed, even the disinterested or
indifferent — as an introduction to what was, by any
objective standards, the most influential Life in human
history. It is also a Life which still speaks profoundly to us,
even in this Third Millennium.

I confess that when the idea for the Jesus Reports first crossed
my mind it was followed close behind by a conviction that it
would never see the light of day. The notion of following
Jesus around, without pre-conception, historical or religious
baggage, and writing about Him as though he were just
another guru trying to muster support, seemed a sure way of
drawing down wrath.

The inclusion of such weekly reports in the *News* pages of the
paper, also seemed to be a bridge which might be difficult
ethically for colleagues to cross, and which could annoy some
readers who might feel that the lines were being blurred
between present and past, fact and (as some would have it)
myth.

When I mentioned the idea to our then *News Editor* Niall
Kiely, as part of a package to mark the year 2000 in The Irish
Times in a particularly Christian way, it was more with
slender hope than solid conviction. But he was enthusiastic.
"*The Editor*," he said, "loved ideas which showed a bit of
imagination." So I went to Conor Brady, whose immediate
response was very positive. He arranged for space to be made

available each Monday, in the *Foreign News* pages as I had asked.

So I found myself with a weekly task which could have become an albatross, but rarely did, even in a year which brought me to Egypt, Turkey, Jordan, Israel, Palestine, Rome, Drumcree (again), and Iran — all in the line of duty. I usually wrote it at my desk in the office on the Friday night before publication. Generally, though not always, I tried to pick passages from the gospels which resonated with events of the previous week. But I set myself the parameter of always remaining close to the gospel account of stories, especially where Jesus is concerned. Only once does He "speak directly" to the reporter, and that was when He "agreed to answer questions for the Mad Chatter Box" report.

In one instance I went close to the edge, suggesting that the miracle at Cana was a prank involving Jesus and Lazarus, while at the same time underpinning the gospel account in two separate reports. But I wanted to suggest that Jesus had a sense of humour. It is difficult to believe that someone so loved by men and women, so popular and charismatic, did not laugh.

The report which elicited the warmest response was probably the one which gives an account of the Samaritan woman meeting Jesus at the well. It seemed to strike a chord with many people, especially women.

Throughout the year I was heartened again and again by the warm response of clergy in particular to what was being attempted. The series also attracted the inevitable raft of abuse, which came from two quarters — those who felt the reports were "an insult to the non-Christian reader of your newspaper" as one writer put it — and those who were scandalised by or misunderstood the approach being taken. One correspondent sent abusive letters, stopping only when some of the more strident comments were put to use in a subsequent report. There were those who expressed disappointment that I should take a traditional view that Mary Magdalene was a prostitute, prompting some correspondence in the *Letters* page of the newspaper.

There is a lot about the media and its methods in the reports. It is a world that I know, and with which people in general are quite familiar. Indeed a friend has suggested that for this very reason, the book might be of interest to media students, which took me by surprise initially, but made sense when reading the reports again.

All in all, writing the series was an enjoyable exercise, and I hope that you, the reader, will enjoy this book.

Patsy McGarry
October 2001

INTRODUCTION

A great story — and the gospel is certainly one — can be told in many ways.

Variety in fact is essential, because no one version can exhaust its meaning. From the very beginning of Christianity believers recognized that the multiple themes of the gospel could not be compressed into a single narrative. The church inherited four gospels, each one different in content, artistry and atmosphere.

Later generations invented new forms in order to keep the gospel alive by retelling it in ways that captured the heart and the imagination. Perhaps the boldest of such attempts to popularize the gospel were the mystery plays of the Middle Ages. They drew on every aspect of contemporary daily life. They were calculated to astonish and to amuse. Thereby they gave the gospel message new life. If it was sometimes bawdy and overblown in keeping with the lusty spirit of the age, it always gave birth to wonder, the state in which we glimpse the Spirit.

Patsy McGarry's *Jesus Reports* is a millennial version of such mystery plays. The crowds of slum-dwellers and peasants are replaced by the characters of his world of journalism—editorial writers, reporters, spokespersons, pundits, and the 'ordinary person' whose views are canvassed for copy.

Since we associate such people with breaking news, this tactic effortlessly draws us into the complex and tumultuous world in which Jesus of Nazareth struggled to make himself heard. McGarry's reconstruction of that world is so vivid that we are battered by the conflicting reactions that Jesus inspired. On which side would we have come down, when authoritative voices claimed that his words were derivative and his miracles only conjuring tricks to dazzle the credulous? Would we have seen beneath the facade of a carpenter's son from Galilee?

Written out of a profound familiarity with the four gospels, and informed by a detailed knowledge of the historical circumstances of the life of Jesus, these reports contain a multitude of insights that illuminate the message of the gospel.

Love was the essence of the preaching of Jesus, and where there is love there is laughter. McGarry rightly refuses to repeat the mistake of the evangelists who permitted reverence to exclude the hints of gentle humour that must have enlivened the daily discourse of Jesus. McGarry restores this indispensable dimension, most often by sly asides that take a moment to sink in, e.g. the identification of Judas Iscariot as "a journalist with the *Palestinian Times*". Occasionally the humour is explicit, as in the desperate plea of the bridegroom at Cana, whose friends have hidden most of the wine bought for the wedding: "Please, fellas. Stop messing."

Much closer to the edge is the hilarious slapstick of the question-and-answer session of the Mad Chatter Box column in the *Cool Press*.

Those who are offended by such pieces should

remember (i) that most biblical scholars consider the Wedding Feast at Cana (John 2:1-12) as an invention of the fourth evangelist; the miracle never really happened; and (ii) that a Cardinal Archbishop recently submitted himself to the same type of impertinent questions on the BBC radio programme "Desert Island Discs"! It completely misses the point to treat such imaginative flights as irreverent and inappropriate. They are nothing of the sort. On the contrary, they embody an authentic Christian challenge to a comfortable complacency that parades as 'respect for religion'.

By drawing attention to such infusions of humour I do not want to give the impression that McGarry's creative ability is limited to inventing funny stories. Much serious thought has gone into these reports and there are flashes of sheer brilliance which guarantee that we shall never read the gospel message in the same way again. His version of the trial of Jesus, for example, is apparently a simple retelling of what we read in the gospels, but it cuts cleanly through to the heart of the matter, and a sense of passionate outrage permeates the words. Only the most insensitive reader can fail to be shocked by the cynicism and the injustice. The words of Jesus are quoted extensively, but occasionally are given new life by a paraphrase of great insight. The Beatitudes, for example, are reformulated as a response to a question of a Pharisee as to who are 'the good guys'. "Jesus replied: 'Those who are poor in spirit; anyone who is grieving; the shy and retiring; whoever cares passionately about injustice; whoever is gentle with the wrongdoer; whoever has an honest intention; peacemakers; and anyone who is persecuted for doing what is right'."

Patsy McGarry is a wonderful teacher, and he is to be warmly congratulated on his success in regenerating the wonder with which we should approach the gospels. Our familiarity is always superficial; new depths are ever there to be plumbed.

Jerome Murphy-O'Connor, OP

Ecole Biblique, Jerusalem

October 2001

Jerome Murphy-O'Connor, OP, a native of Cork, is Professor of New Testament at the Ecole Biblique, Jerusalem, where he was the first non-Frenchman to be invited to join the faculty.

He entered the Dominican Order in 1953 and studied in Cork before being ordained in 1960. He did his doctorate in New Testament Studies at Fribourg University in Switzerland, after which he went to Jerusalem. He spends his summers lecturing around the world, but always finds time for a few weeks in Cork as well.

He is recognised as a world expert on the historical Jesus and the life of Paul. Besides his books, Paul: A Critical Life *(1996) and* The Holy Land: An Oxford Archaeological Guide *from Earliest Times to 1700 (fourth edition, 1997), he is the author of numerous scholarly articles and a contributor to* The New Jerome Biblical Commentary. *In addition he has been adviser to the recent 10-part ITV* Apostles *and BBC* Son of God *series, and played a prominent part in Sky TV's coverage of the Pope's visit to the Holy Land in 2000.*

Herod marriage criticised by "Baptist" John

GALILEE, 30 AD

A spokesman for Herod, tetrarch of Galilee, has denounced as "further authoritarian righteousness" a condemnation of his marriage by the preacher John. Herod recently married Herodias, the former wife of his brother Philip, tetrarch of Ituraea and Trachonitis. John, known locally as "the Baptist" because of his practice of pouring water on sinners, has been attracting large crowds along the edge of the Judaean desert where he is said to live. He has consistently condemned Herod for alleged abuses of power.

The Galilean tetrarch's spokesman said last night that John's condemnation of Herod's marriage went beyond the bounds of normal public discourse. "Surely the private lives of public figures ought to be their business alone, as it is with everybody else," he said.

"This is just another example of the distasteful neo-puritanism now sweeping the country and which seems to consider everyone in authority fair game for the ugliest scrutiny."

The spokesman agreed that recent financial and sexual scandals, allegedly involving Herod, had contributed to this atmosphere but he insisted that the intolerance of human frailty now so evident on the part of "these so-called prophets on the margins of life and society" could lead to greater abuses. "It is a recipe for tyranny, the tyranny of a rigid orthodoxy," he said.

The High Priest, Dr Caiaphas, declined to comment on the controversy. However, a source close to his office said that though it could be said Herod's relationship with Herodias may not be in accordance with the laws of God, this was difficult to prove.

"How do we know the nature of their partnership?" he asked. "It is possible, after all, that it has not been consummated. But we can only know if the couple wishes to talk about it, and they obviously do not. The alternative, if we are to know the truth, is to spy in their bedroom, which is as patently ridiculous as it is unseemly. It is best such matters are left to the mercy and wisdom of God." His strongest criticisms, however, were for the preacher John.

"We have had a plethora of those self-styled prophets and even messiahs these past months, and it is time the civil authorities dealt with them. Any vagabond—and usually with no visible means of support—can, it seems, claim to be speaking as God or in his name and get away with it. Everywhere they create discontent among the people, attacking lawful authority, religious as well as civic."

Speaking last night, John denied he had ever claimed to be the Messiah. He said he would not be fit even to tie the Messiah's sandals, but he did agree that some of his followers claimed he was the one sent by God. "I try to stop them but they won't listen," he said.

Herod marriage criticised by "baptist" John
For the setting of these and their dates see The Gospel According to Saint Luke

(Lk) 3:1-2. For John's ministry (up to baptism of Jesus) look at The Gospel According to Saint Matthew (Mt) 3:1-12; The Gospel According to Saint Mark (Mk) 1:1-8; and also Lk 3:2-18; as well as The Gospel According to Saint John (Jn) 1:19-28. For John the Baptist's proscription of Herod and Herodias, see Mt 14:3-5; Mk 6:17-20; Lk 3:19-20. John denies he is the Messiah, at Mt 3:11-12; Mk 1:7-8; Lk 3:16-17; Jn 1:20-27.

"Bitter young man"
attacks sects

Bethany, 30 AD

The preacher John has denounced the various religious denominations among his people as "a collection of snakes". Speaking to a crowd of many hundreds in Bethany yesterday, he told Pharisees and Sadducees, sent to question him by the religious leadership in Jerusalem, that the axe of God's judgement was raised and would chop down and throw every bad tree among them into the fire.

In his most virulent attack yet, he warned them that they were not to think they would escape God's judgement just because of who they were. "Chaff will be separated from grain and the chaff will be burned in eternal fire," he told them. John has already attacked the denominations for their obsession with appearances rather than truth.

"A bitter young man," said Bartholomew, a Pharisee. Mary, a young woman from Bethany, retorted: "He's just saying what we all know but haven't the courage to say." Her sister Martha wished there were more men like John. "Then we'd all be better off," she said.

There are three denominations or sects among John's people. The Pharisees believe in strict observance of tradition and what they conclude is the written law of God. Many say they tend to see themselves as morally superior. The Sadducees do not believe in the resurrection of the dead. They do not accept that angels and spirits exist and reject obligations in the unwritten law which the Pharisees say have been handed down by tradition from Moses. The third denomination, the Essenes—the one John has been least critical of—live a quiet, simple, ascetic life.

Paul, a cheerful, plump young man from the village of Kroc in the south and a follower of John, said: "We are entering a post-denominational era where the differences between denominations will be irrelevant. Anyway, people are sick and tired of the way these guys cling to their divisions and appeal to the rest of us to respect those divisions. Then, at the same time, they tell us all they want is unity! No wonder John calls them hypocrites."

Over recent weeks, John has been preaching to large crowds along the Jordan river and near the desert in Judaea. He is said to live there on locusts and wild honey. He dresses in clothes made from camel hair. He has denied he is the Messiah. "I am a voice crying in the wilderness," he told the crowd, "preparing a way for the Lord. Level the mountains! Fill up the valleys! Straighten the curves! Smooth out the ruts!"

"That fella should be in politics," remarked Philip, a Sadducee. "He wouldn't survive long," said his friend Nathanael. "He'd soon have opponents come looking for his head."

Zebedee, who had been visiting friends in Bethany, said: "What he needs is a couple of days fishing on the lake [Galilee] with my two lads James and John and then to go chasing girls with them in the evenings. That'd sort him out."

"Something decent to eat would be more like it," said Alphaeus, a Pharisee. "No man could be right on just locusts and honey. And then wearing that camel hair stuff!" Anna, a cousin of Zebedee's, disagreed. "He's a classic case of the 'only child' syndrome," she said. "Spoiled rotten by elderly parents. Unable to cope when they died. So he escaped to the desert where he could be king of everything again." She began to cough.

Anna had come to Bethany believing John would cure her fever. John had asked her to get into the river to be baptised. She refused. "I'm bad enough as it is," she told him. "That'd be the death of me altogether."

She was not impressed with John. "Would you look at him," she said. "How could anyone as miserable as that be any use?" And she set off for Galilee where she lives with her daughter Miriam and son-in-law Simon. Zebedee followed her.

"If you have two coats, give one to the poor," John preached. "You tax collectors, take from the people what the government requires you to, and no more. You soldiers, don't extort money and be content with your pay."

Paul complained that lately many people had been drifting to another preacher further down the river. "He is very popular," he said. But he didn't know his name.

"Bitter young man" attacks sects
A general account of John's ministry is to be found in Mt 3:1–12; Mk 1:2–8; Lk 3:1–18 and Jn 1:19-27. For his warning to the Pharisees and Sadducees look at Mt 3:7-10 and Lk 3:7-9. Compare these words of John's with those of Jesus in Jn 8:33–39 and Jn 15:2–6. A description of John's lifestyle is to be found in Mt 3:4 and Mk 1:6. For John's advice to different groups see Lk 3:10-14.

Rumours of a new eccentric Baptist

Judaea, 30 AD

The preacher John has denied speculation that he has given up his mission and is retiring to Galilee. "As long as there is breath in my body I intend to do the work of God," he said last night. Yesterday he continued to baptise people in the Jordan and would be doing so for the foreseeable future, he said. This practice, of pouring water on sinners, has led to him being nicknamed "the Baptist" locally.

The speculation, that at 30 years of age he was to take early retirement, is believed to have been fuelled by an incident at the Jordan last Wednesday when he baptised a fellow preacher.

Philip, a Sadducee from the village of Bethsaida, explained that "this fellow—about the same age as 'the Baptist'—came out of nowhere and John seemed to hero-worship him. It was amazing. You know John, he bows to no one. But he was like a child. Anyway this other preacher asked to be baptised by him and John refused. He said it should be the other way round."

Nathanael, a friend of Philip's, said: "I couldn't believe my ears. A humble John, I ask you? But the other fellow insisted. John gave in and baptised him. Then the two of them stopped and stared up into the blue sky. It was weird."

"Jesus," said Paul, a follower of John's. "That's his name—the other preacher. And they weren't staring into the blue sky. John said a dove appeared over Jesus's head just as he was baptising him and God said from Heaven: 'This is my dear son. He's a fine fellow'.

"John says Jesus is the one he was sent to prepare the way for. 'He has surpassed me because he was before me,' he told us, whatever that means."

Nathanael said it sounded like a friendly takeover to him.

Bartholomew, a Pharisee who joined the group as Paul was explaining about the baptism of Jesus, commented that he always knew John wasn't half right. "All that locusts and camel hair stuff." But any doubts he had were now "well and truly gone. He's off his rocker. Seeing birds and hearing voices. It's time he gave it up."

"Anytime a pigeon hovered over my head it wasn't water I was covered in," said Nathanael. "It wasn't a pigeon, it was a dove," said Paul, "but it's worse than that." And he told them Jesus was from Nazareth. The other three men laughed.

Bartholomew commented: "Need I say more?"

Philip said: "Sure nothing decent ever came out of Nazareth." And he thought it extraordinary that John would defer to anyone from there. "This is the man whose sandals he is not fit to tie? I just don't believe it," he said.

Paul said: "It's even worse. John said Jesus descended from Adam, through Noah, Abraham, King David, and Joshua. And, even worse again, he said Jesus is the Son of God." The other three seemed to laugh for an age. Catching breath, Bartholomew said: "Ah, well … that's that."

"God is a Jew. Right?" blurted Nathanael. "And he has a son. Right? Can you imagine any Jewish father saying to anybody 'This is my dear son. He's a fine fellow'?" as he quoted God in an attempted stern, bass tone.

Bartholomew remarked that he never realised "the old man got up to that sort of thing. I wonder has he any daughters?"

Paul, who had been silent through all this hilarity, said he was depressed and deeply disappointed in John. He felt "the Baptist" was taking a back seat. He was going back to his cousins in Kroc, he said, and left.

"Now there goes a young man growing up," said Bartholomew.

Rumours of a new eccentric baptist
Accounts of John's meeting with Jesus and the Baptism of Jesus are to be found in Mt 3:13–17; Mk 1:9–11; Lk 3:21–23. For a different perspective on these events see Jn 1:28–34. Look also at Jn 3:22–36. For Nathanael's views on Nazareth, see Jn 1:43–51.

MIRACLE CURE
RUMOURS ATTRACT CROWDS

JUDAEA, 30 AD

Reports have been circulating in Jerusalem all week about miracles attributed to Jesus, the preacher from Nazareth. Crowds of the sick and their relatives are said to be following him wherever he goes. He is believed to have pleaded with people it is claimed he has cured that they keep it to themselves.

Thaddaeus from the village of Nain in Galilee said last night he had leprosy for more than seven years before he heard of Jesus. He spent days travelling around the province before he finally caught up with Jesus, he said. "I had nothing to lose. I was covered in sores from head to foot."

He had great difficulty pushing his way through the crowds. "I begged him, I got on my knees and I begged him. I said, 'Jesus, you know that if you want to, you can cure me. Please, please make me clean.' And, I don't mind saying, I cried. Anyhow, Jesus said he wanted to help me. He had tears in his eyes and he touched my shoulder. He said 'Be clean'— and the leprosy disappeared. Just like that. I doubt if I had a happier moment in my entire life. You have no idea what it is like," he said.

Afterwards, as Jesus moved away through the crowds, he turned and called back to Thaddaeus. "Don't tell anyone about this. You can see it is bad enough already," he said pointing at the crowd. "But show yourself to the priests," he said.

Thaddaeus, however, could not stop telling people about what had happened to him. "How could I be expected to keep something like that to myself?" he asked, "And there were all the people who knew me beforehand. I had to explain to them why I was so different."

But he was sorry for doing so, he said. He had heard the crowds following Jesus had got even bigger as news of his cure spread.

It has since been reported that Jesus no longer enters a town in daylight, to avoid drawing such numbers. He is believed to retreat often to any quiet spot he can find, and has disappeared for days at a time. But roving crowds continue to search for him everywhere. Currently his exact whereabouts are unknown, though it is believed he may still be in Galilee.

The authorities are keeping a close eye on the situation but so far there have been no reports of any public disorder. A spokesman for the Governor of Palestine, Mr Pilate, said last night that for now there was nothing to worry about. In fact they were more concerned about the reaction of the religious leadership in the country to the increasing popularity of Jesus, he said. But as far as the governor was concerned, there would be no problem as long as Jesus was not responsible for any major disruptions.

Mr Pilate was in Bethlehem with his officials yesterday as part of an initiative to bring government closer to the regions. The visit was marred by protesting shepherds who claimed the army was not paying them enough for mutton.

"Don't wash your hands of this too," read a placard, referring to Mr Pilate's habit of washing his hands in public when the local authorities make decisions he either disagrees with or has no say in. He has been accused again recently of allowing colleagues "hang out to dry".

Meanwhile, the religious authorities have been busy attending annual denominational unity week services involving the Pharisees and Sadducees mainly. While some small progress has been made, unity is not much closer than it was. However, it is still felt important that the event should take place, even if it is little more than a formality.

When contacted last night, a spokesman for the High Priest, Dr Caiaphas, was dismissive of Jesus. "He's from Nazareth," he pointed out. He described him as "just the latest freak people have decided to follow". He said there was "absolutely no proof" that any miracles had been performed by him. He suggested that in instances where an individual's condition may have improved following contact with the preacher, it would more than likely be found to be "perfectly rationally explicable".

Faith-healing was not unusual in Palestine, he said. And such was the power of the mind that in instances it was possible that individuals had actually willed themselves better. "But all this talk of miracles is irresponsible. It excites innocent, ignorant people and will cause trouble yet. So if I were Jesus I'd go easy on the miracles," he said.

Miracle cure rumours attract crowds
Compare this report with Mt 4:23–25; Mt 8:1–4 and Mt 4:12–17; Mk 1:21–34; Lk 5:12–15.

SHARED DRINK AT WELL STIRS THE WATERS

JUDAEA, 30 AD

There has been heated debate in Palestine this week following a front-page headline in the *Moon* tabloid on Wednesday: "Sups with scum—claims he is Messiah!"

The report, billed as an "exclusive", concerned an encounter between the preacher Jesus and a Samaritan woman at a drinking place known as "Jacob's Well". It is near Sychar on the border between Judaea and Samaria.

According to local sources, at about midday on Monday, Jesus stopped at the well. It is near a plot of ground local people say the Patriarch Jacob gave to his son Joseph.

A Samaritan woman came to get water. Jesus asked her for a drink. She was shocked. She knew Jews despised Samaritans and, besides, she was a woman. "You're a Jew and I am a Samaritan woman. How can you ask me for a drink just like that?" she asked. He said that if she knew who he was, it was she who would be asking him for a drink instead.

"Everyone who drinks this water will be thirsty again," he said, pointing to the well, "but whoever drinks the water I give them will never be thirsty." She asked for some of that sort of water. He told her to get her husband and come back. "I have no husband," she said.

He said he knew. "The fact is you have had five husbands and the man you live with now is not your husband either," he said. She was astounded. How could he possibly know this?

"You are a prophet," she said eventually and, as if to

excuse herself and her people, added: "We worship on this mountain but you Jews say we should worship in the Temple in Jerusalem." He reassured her. "Take no heed," he said. "The time is coming when you will worship God neither on this mountain nor in Jerusalem. God is spirit and his worshippers will worship in spirit. Anywhere."

But the woman was confused. She was used to worshipping God in one place. "When the Messiah comes he will explain it to us, I suppose," she said. And Jesus said: "I am he."

At that point his friends returned from Sychar where they had gone for food. They saw the Samaritan woman but said nothing. She ran off, and in such a hurry she left her water jar behind.

The friends tried to get Jesus to eat but he wouldn't. They wondered whether he had eaten already. "No," he said. "I have food you know nothing about," he said, "my food is to do what I was sent to do, and to finish the job." And they hadn't a clue what he meant.

Just then the Samaritan woman arrived back with a crowd of people from Sychar. "He told me everything I ever did," she said, exaggerating in her excitement.

Some of the people spoke to Jesus and asked him to stay with them for a while. He stayed for two days. By then they were saying, as quoted in the *Moon*, "we believe he really is the Saviour. Not because of anything she said, but because we have heard him ourselves."

The *Moon* report described the woman as "a slut" and the people from Sychar as "stupid Samaritan peasants conned by a crazy Nazarene". In an editorial on Thursday, the *Palestinian Times* described the *Moon* headline and report as "racist, an affront to human rights, and a new low in Palestinian journalism". It called on the authorities to take immediate action against the tabloid.

A spokesman for the Governor, Mr Pilate, said last night that the *Moon* report and headline "certainly were inflammatory", but that the matter seemed to have settled down. It was not proposed to take any action, he said.

A spokesman for the High Priest, Dr Caiaphas, said that while such news reporting was "unacceptable" it was not surprising that it should happen in a situation where sects were proliferating all over the country and messiahs seemed to be "as plentiful as olives on a tree".

He condemned Jesus—and for associating with a Samaritan woman. It pained him to use the word "perverted", when talking about a Jew associating with Samaritans and treating them as equals before God. "But that is what it is," he said.

The editor of the *Moon*, James Iscariot jnr, dismissed the *Palestinian Times* editorial as "predictable moralising from that quarter. They say their paper's motto is 'treating everyone equally'," he said, "and they do. They look down on us all." He was happy his own newspaper had lived up to its motto: "Reflecting the truth as it is."

Shared drink at well stirs the water
This event at Jacob's Well near Sychar in Samaria is reported by Saint John, see Jn 4:4–42.

ZEALOT TOLD TO PUT HIS SWORD AWAY

GALILEE, 30 AD

His name is Simon. He is a Zealot, and he has had a falling out with Jesus the preacher. "He wouldn't let me go along with him," he said. "I pleaded with him, I begged him, I never met anyone like him."

He was speaking on the shores of Lake Galilee at a spot where Jesus had been preaching to large crowds just hours beforehand. Simon was torn. "When he puts his hand on your shoulder it's as if he sees no one else in the whole wide world; that he'd do anything for you. You just know you could trust him with your life. And you want to," he said.

Simon wanted to. He wanted to even as he spoke, he said. But he is a Zealot. Jesus had said repeatedly to him: "Put away your sword, put away your sword, and then you can be with me and my friends." Simon paused before saying, "but I can't put away my sword".

He is a young man about the same age as Jesus. He had been involved with the Zealot guerrillas in a long campaign against the Romans.

There has been peace in Palestine recently. "Putting away the sword for me is the same thing as saying I accept the right of the Roman army of occupation to be in our country. I've sacrificed too much, trying to get them out, for that. I've seen too many great friends killed, to be able to turn around now and say it was all for nothing. So … we might have won a few concessions for our people, but how can we guarantee these will last?" he said.

He was surprised that Jesus was being "so unreasonable". "I mean he's a Jew too. Surely he can't be happy with this situation either," he said. He had put it to Jesus, who said the Romans and those like them were children of this world and valued only what was here. He and those who wanted to be with him belonged to God and the things of His world.

"'Empires come and go. God is forever,' he said, or something like that," Simon recalled. "'Put away your sword, Simon, and you are welcome to come with me,' he said." Simon pleaded that he had no intention of using the sword. He hadn't used it in years. He needed it just in case he or his people were attacked again. But Jesus was having none of it. He told him to put his trust in him and in God, rather than in the weapons of this world. Simon asked for time to think about it. He is thinking about it. He is in difficulty.

Further ahead along the lake shore larger and larger crowds followed Jesus as he walked northwards in the direction of the town of Capernaum. The people had heard so many stories of miraculous cures attributed to him that everywhere, as now, they crowded in on him, out of hope and curiosity.

He noticed two boats on the lake shore. He asked a fisherman if he'd mind taking him a few yards out into the water in one of them so he could preach without being jostled. The fisherman said it was no trouble at all. His name was Simon also. Like James and John, Simon is a common name among Jewish men in the province of Galilee. Which is why local people use nicknames so much.

When Jesus had finished preaching he asked Simon to row out into deeper water and let down his nets. Simon was reluctant. "We've been on the lake all night and didn't catch a thing. There's nothing out there," he said, "but, if it'll make you happy …" So, along with his brother Andrew, he rowed deep into the lake and let the nets down.

As they hauled the nets back Simon realised they were so full of fish they would need help. He shouted across the water to their fishing partners John and James, sons of Zebedee. They were standing on the shore beside the other boat. They came out on the lake and soon both boats were so full of fish they began to sink.

Simon was overwhelmed by it all. He fell to his knees in front of Jesus and said: "I don't deserve this. You are far too good to the likes of me." And Jesus said to him "It's all right, Simon. From now on it's people you will catch."

And when they eventually got to the shore, all four men left everything just there and went with Jesus to Capernaum, which is also their home town.

Zealot told to put his sword away
For the call of the first disciples of Jesus, see Mt 4:18–22; Mk 1:16–20; Lk 5:1–11. John (1:35–42) gives a different perspective.

GROWING BAND FOLLOWS PREACHER

GALILEE, 30 AD

Speculation has been growing in Galilee this week that the preacher Jesus is setting up a new sect to promote his own brand of Judaism. He has gathered around him a group of young men and women who help deal with the crowds following him everywhere. They also relay what he is saying to those who can't get within hearing range.

Last week he was seen entering the town of Capernaum on the shores of Lake Galilee accompanied by a group of fishermen. These included the brothers Simon and Andrew, originally from Bethsaida further north on the lakeshore, and two other brothers, James and John, sons of Zebedee, one of the best-known fishermen in Capernaum.

Jesus calls Simon, the older of the young men, "Peter". At the beginning it was thought this was a nickname to differentiate him from all the other Simons in Galilee, but he said it was because Peter would be his rock, his main man.

Simon Peter is married to Miriam, a member of one of Capernaum's best known families. Her mother Anna lives with them, and one of the strangest events of the week centred on her. She had a high fever for a long time and none of the usual remedies helped.

Local sources say that, on Tuesday, Simon Peter brought Jesus to see her. She was dismissive. "All you preacher fellows are quacks as far as I'm concerned," she said, and turned to the wall. Simon Peter was embarrassed. Jesus laughed.

"Anna, give me your hand like a good woman," he said. "Sure you have nothing to lose." Slowly, she turned to them, perspiration rolling from her forehead. "I suppose that's true," she said and raised her left hand which Jesus took in his. She felt better immediately. Within a half hour she was out of the bed and fussing.

"You must be starving, you poor man," she said and went to the kitchen. "Simon," she roared back, "will you get Miriam." And so began a swirl of activity as the children were put to bed and the women prepared food for Jesus and his friends. James and John wanted to go home but Anna insisted they stay to celebrate her recovery. Much wine was drunk.

"He's the real thing. Where did you get him?" she is said to have asked Simon Peter when Jesus had left. And Peter explained about the crowds and the boat and the fish and the walk to Capernaum and how Jesus wanted him, Andrew, James and John to help him spread his message and how he would love to do so but was worried about Miriam and the children and how they would be in his absence. "... And he calls me Peter," he said.

"He does, does he!" said Anna. "It means 'rock!'," said Peter. And she laughed. "What's the other word for 'sand'?" she asked, and Miriam got angry. "Mother, only for Simon you'd still be sick in bed. You just can't leave him alone, can you?" Anna, however, was in form. "Well it's the first right thing he's done since you married him," she said. "Rock is it? Sure he'd let down even his own mother, and when she needed him most. You can't rely on him. And now he wants to go off, leaving you and the kids. What sort of man is he at all?" She is believed to have said.

It is understood the other men began to leave quietly then. Peter reassured Miriam. Her mother's remarks ran off him like water off a fish, he said. "Don't let it bother you." And Miriam encouraged him to go with Jesus if that was what he wanted to do. "We'll be fine," she said, "and it'll probably only be for a little while anyway."

Growing band follows preacher
See Mt 8:14–15; Mk 1:29–31; Lk 4:38–39 as well as Lk 5:27–28.

ZEALOTS BLAMED FOR HECKLER'S PROTEST

CAPERNAUM, 30 AD

A possibly dangerous situation was pre-empted in Capernaum yesterday when a protester began shouting at the preacher Jesus as he spoke in the synagogue. The protester shouted: "What are you doing here, Jesus of Nazareth? Why are you annoying us. Are you going to destroy us with your nonsense?"

A woman, standing nearby, said to her friend: "The devil is in that fellow." John, a friend of Jesus, was very angry. He told his brother James he believed the interruption was deliberately timed to cause Jesus maximum embarrassment. He believed the protester was a Zealot. "They should all be locked up," he said.

But Jesus was not said to be embarrassed. "Be quiet," he ordered, and with such force it took the protester by complete surprise. He began to shake violently and fell to the floor shrieking. "I told you the devil was in him," said the woman to her friend.

Soon the man was still. He looked around like someone waking from sleep, and was helped to his feet by people standing nearby. He was calm. "God …," said the woman to her friend, "he [Jesus] can even order the devil around."

Later that day three young men—Philip and Nathanael with their friend, Bartholomew—were passing through Capernaum on their way home to Bethsaida, north of the lake, when they saw Jesus. They were in high spirits as usual.

Philip recognised Jesus from the time he saw him baptised in the river Jordan by the preacher John. "Yo, there goes the son of God," he said. Nathanael lay against a fig tree.

"Hey, it's Simon," said Philip, recognising Peter, "and Andrew." Peter and Andrew also came from Bethsaida. "Yo, Simon," Philip shouted as they came closer. "… Peter," said Peter. "Philip! You eejit. Don't you recognise me, for God's sake?" asked Philip. And Peter explained he did but that his own name had been changed by Jesus and how he was now helping Jesus with his campaign.

Nathanael was disgusted. "If 'Simon' is good enough for Bethsaida it's good enough for anyone from a kip like Nazareth," he said. But Peter did not want a row. He said he would bring them to meet Jesus. "Yeah, I've always wanted to meet the son of God," said Nathanael.

Peter ignored the mockery and said: "We're all sons of God."

As they went towards Jesus, it is believed Peter told the three about the scene in the synagogue and the protester shouting. "… Every son of God gets a bit of hard luck sometimes…," sang Bartholomew, from a song by their friend Loudan. "… Especially when he goes around saying he's the way," continued Nathanael.

As they got closer, Jesus came towards them and said: "Ah, Nathanael …," and he turned to the crowd. "Here is one true son of Israel."

Nathanael was stunned. "How do you know me?" he asked Jesus. "I saw you over there under that fig tree with Philip…"

All three young men were totally shocked. How could he have known? Noticing their reaction Jesus is said to have replied: "Don't be surprised at this. It's nothing. Ye'll see far greater things I tell you."

Philip, Nathanael and Bartholomew later joined with the rest of the band of friends who now go everywhere with Jesus.

APOLOGY

In a previous Jesus Report, serious doubt was cast on the character of Peter. This publication wishes to dissociate itself entirely from those comments. We are satisfied that Peter is a man of the highest integrity and a most loyal, dependable friend and relative.

By agreement with Iscariot and Iscariot (Capernaum) Solicitors, a substantial sum has been donated to the Galilee Fishermen's Provident Fund.

Zealots blamed for heckler's protest
See Mk 1:21–28; Mk 2:1–12 and Lk 4:31–37. For the matter of the witness of John the Baptist and the call of the first disciples read the account in Jn 1:15–51 and look at Lk 6:13–16.

KINGS FROM EAST TRICK HEROD

JERUSALEM, 30 AD

The authorities in Judaea have reacted with fury to a story in the current issue of *Magi* magazine which claims that the late King Herod, father of the current king, ordered a massacre of children in Bethlehem almost 30 years ago. "This is an outrageous suggestion," he said and insisted legal action was being considered.

He described a call by the magazine for an inquiry to be set up to investigate the slaughter as "preposterous".

According to the *Magi* report three kings from the east, who had come to Judaea around that time, sought permission from King Herod to journey further into the country.

They said they had seen a star which, as astrologers, they maintained indicated a child had been born who was destined to be king of the Jews. They had followed the star as far as Jerusalem and wished to continue further into the country.

According to *Magi* sources King Herod was deeply disturbed by the kings' story. He called his advisers who told him that it had been foretold that such a child would be born in Bethlehem.

King Herod informed the three eastern kings of this. He advised them to go to Bethlehem, find the child and let him know the details as he would like to visit it too. The kings followed the star until it stopped over Bethlehem.

When they arrived at the cave they went inside and found a baby boy being fed by his mother, a young woman called Mary. The kings presented expensive gifts for which Mary was very grateful.

Afterwards, as the kings were about to return to Herod in Jerusalem, one of them said he had an instinct that would be dangerous. The late King Herod had a reputation for paranoia and dealt violently with rivals or anyone he suspected might become one. The kings went back to their countries by a different route.

Magi reported that, when he heard this, King Herod was furious and ordered that every boy in Bethlehem below the age of two be killed. A witness was quoted by *Magi* as saying: "We were stunned that he (King Herod) would even think of doing such a thing. But no one would stand up to him. When he was like that it would have been suicide."

The spokesman for the current King Herod accused *Magi* of "gutter journalism" and said it was taking advantage of current laws, which hold the dead cannot be libelled, to print "a sensational story to boost its declining circulation, and in the process attempt to ruin the reputation of one of Judaea's greatest kings."

In a further development, the *Palestinian Times* has reported that it is claimed the child the three kings visited in Bethlehem escaped to Egypt and is the preacher Jesus. An article by the newspaper's Religious Affairs Correspondent, Mr Judas Iscariot, reported that, Jesus, his mother Mary and her partner Joseph went to Egypt as soon as the three kings left.

The article, based on an interview with a friend of Jesus's, said Joseph had been told King Herod expressed an interest in visiting them too and, aware of the king's reputation, became afraid.

That night they set off for Egypt and stayed there for four years until the king died. They then returned to Palestine and went to live in Nazareth.

Last night a spokesman for the High Priest, Dr Caiaphas, described the *Palestinian Times* story as "a joke". "Can't you see what these guys are doing?" he said. "They have studied the prophets and have reinvented the fellow's childhood so he fits in with predictions about the Messiah. It's a disgrace."

He suggested that John, a friend of Jesus, was probably behind the story. John had a reputation for cleverness, he said. "I can see his footprints all over that (*Times*) article—the prints of darkness!" he said.

However, it has since transpired that the source of the piece was Matthew, a former tax collector and another friend of Jesus's.

Kings from East trick Herod
The account of this visit by the kings from the East is found only in Mt 2:1–12. How Joseph took his family into Egypt is narrated at Mt 2:13–23.

Losers, Wimps Hailed as "Good Guys"

A mountain, Galilee, 30 AD

The preacher Jesus has denied that a programme he outlined yesterday is "a charter for losers". The criticism was levelled at him by a Pharisee who was among thousands at a rally Jesus held on a mountainside near Lake Galilee which was one of the most significant in his campaign.

Jesus strongly opposes the use of the word "campaign" in connection with his addresses throughout Palestine. It has annoyed him and his friends that media continue to do so, particularly the *Moon* tabloid which insists Jesus wants to be "King of the Jews".

On the mountainside, as Jesus began denouncing the hypocrisy of Pharisees, a member of the sect challenged him. "We've heard all this already. We know who the bad guys are—us—but who are the good guys?"

Jesus replied: "Those who are poor in spirit; anyone who is grieving; the shy and retiring; whoever cares passionately about justice; whoever is gentle with the wrongdoer; whoever has an honest intention; peacemakers; and anyone who is persecuted for doing what is right."

"Ah, Jesus!" interjected the Pharisee. "Wimps? Losers? They're your good guys?"

They are "the salt of the earth," said Jesus, "the light of the world ... a city on a hill that cannot be hidden."

"A poet, and he doesn't know it," mocked the Pharisee to the crowd, now enjoying the exchange. He then asked whether Jesus wanted to abolish the law of Moses.

Jesus said he was there to fulfil the law, not to abolish it. The Pharisee laughed. "The arrogance," he said. Jesus pointed at him and said: "I tell you that unless your goodness is more than that of your kind and the teachers of the law you will never get to heaven."

The Pharisee was angry. But Jesus was in full spate. "The law says 'do not murder', but I tell you that whoever is even angry with someone will be judged harshly ..."

Moving to the sixth commandment, he said: "You have heard it said, 'don't commit adultery'. I am telling you that even if you look lustfully at another person you have already committed adultery." There was a murmur from the crowd. Some shouted at Jesus that he was crazy. The Pharisee said Jesus would be left with eunuchs and bloodless wonders as followers.

"If your eye causes you to sin, pluck it out," continued Jesus, "or your arm or any part of your body ... cut it off and throw it away."

"Anyone who divorces, except for infidelity, causes the other partner to be an adulterer, and anyone who marries that other partner also becomes an adulterer," Jesus continued. People began to walk away.

"He's lost it," said the Pharisee. "He's finished."

But he wasn't. Jesus told them: "Don't swear by heaven or the earth or by God or by Jerusalem or by your head. Just let 'yes' be yes, and 'no' be no ..."

"By God!" said the Pharisee. Jesus continued: "You've heard it said, 'An eye for an eye and a tooth for a tooth', but

I tell you if someone hits you in the face, turn the other cheek. Love your enemies. Pray for those who persecute you ..."

"Lie down and let them walk all over you," interjected the Pharisee.

"Keep your good deeds private and when you pray keep that private too," said Jesus. "Keep it simple. Say something like this: 'Our father in heaven, that you may be praised; that your reign on earth will be the same as in heaven. Give us what we need today. Forgive us our wrongs, as we forgive those who wrong us. Help us avoid temptation and the devil.'

"Remember you can't serve God and money. Don't worry about the future. Tomorrow will look after itself. And don't judge people. Do to them what you would like to be done to yourself. Ask, and God will give to you. But beware of false prophets. You will know them by their fruits," and he had finished.

"Not a hope," commented the Pharisee. "He's going nowhere. It'll never catch on."

Losers, wimps hailed as "good guys"
Look at Mt 5:1–48; Mt 6:24–34; Mt 7:15–20 and Lk 6:17–49.
For Jesus's advice on prayer see Mt 6:1–15 and Lk 11:1–13.

Call for laws to curb religious "frauds"

Judaea, 30 AD

Reports that the preacher Jesus has disappeared have been greeted with consternation and derision in Palestine. "Missing but not missed," read a front-page headline in the *Moon* tabloid.

It quoted an anonymous source in the religious leadership as saying: "Good riddance. But it is time the Governor introduced a law to stop these frauds from stirring up the people as this Jesus freak was doing."

The source also called for action against the baptist, John. "In no other civilised country would the things he has said about the king and the chief priests be tolerated," he said.

However, many people who had been following Jesus were devastated. They included a Roman centurion called Patrick. "I had hoped he might cure my favourite servant," he said. But Jesus's close friends remained very casual about his disappearance.

"... Weird!" said John. "What's weird about it?" asked Peter. "You know he has done this before. Forty days in the desert once. Time out, to talk to his father. What's weird about that?"

"I don't mean that," said John. "It's the name. Patrick." Nathanael said it was very common among the Roman soldiers in Bethsaida, his home town. "It means 'noble' in Latin, one of them told me," he said, "but he was probably joking."

"You won't hear any decent Jew with that name," said Bartholomew, "nor any friend of mine or of Jesus. Who wants to be called after an invader in an army of occupation?" He told them graffiti near his home read "Patrick Go Home." "Mild enough," commented Nathanael.

"He talks to his father in the desert?" said James. "I thought his father was in Nazareth where he was born." "He wasn't born in Nazareth, and Joseph is not his real father," interjected his brother John. "You just don't get it, do you, James?"

James said he read in the *Palestinian Times* that Jesus was born in Nazareth, "and it is always right," he said.

"It's no more weird than Zebedee," said Bartholomew, still talking about the name Patrick. "Leave our old man out of this," said James, referring to his and John's father, Zebedee. "Yeah, but it's weird," said Bartholomew. James was angry. "Cool it," said John to him, which made James even more angry.

"You never stand up for Dad," said James. "... And you were always Daddy's boy," said John. And they were fighting again. "You just never forgave him for being easy on me that time," said James to John. And he told the others the story of how, a couple of years before, he had squandered his inheritance on drink and women in Jerusalem. Soon he was so desperate "I took a job cleaning pigs and even ate what they were fed," he said.

"Here we go again," chimed in John, sick of the story.

"He doesn't like to hear it because he comes out of it in his true colours," said James. And he told how he was in such despair he decided to risk his father's anger and go home. "And as I came near our house in Capernaum I saw the old man in the distance and he saw me and he came running to me with his arms outstretched and I ran to him and we hugged each other there, both of us crying like babies." And he began to cry again at the memory.

"There we go again," said John.

"And you ... you!" interjected James. Turning to the others he said: "Do you know what he did when the old man ordered that a big feast be prepared and that the best calf we owned be killed and cooked to celebrate my return, do you know what he did?"

He answered his own question: "He sulked. He complained to Dad. 'I have been here all the time slaving for you and you never had a feast for me, boo hoo'," he said, mimicing John.

"You always were Dad's favourite," said John. "You'd get away with murder where I'd be fleeced." Peter was annoyed at the two of them.

"For the love of God will ye stop it. Two grown men going on like this. Sometimes I wonder about Jesus's judgement when I hear this sort of carry-on."

Then both brothers turned on Peter. "We worry about his judgement too when he calls you his 'rock'," said John. "'Peter' indeed!" muttered James. "Rock my foot." And James and John were friends again.

Call for laws to curb religious "frauds"
See Mt 8:5–13; Mt 4:1–11; Mt 1:18–25; Mt 2:1–23; Mk 1:12–13. For the story of the prodigal son, look at Lk 15:11–32.

WATER, WINE AND A SENSE OF HUMOUR

BETHANY, 30 AD

A close friend of the preacher Jesus, who has not been seen for weeks, has said he is probably in the Judaean desert praying. "He goes in for that sort of thing lately," said Lazarus, a wine maker in Bethany. "There's a serious side to him and now and again he needs to get away."

Lazarus explained that Jesus had been a friend since both were very young. "Myself and my two sisters, Martha and Mary, used spend our summers with cousins in Nazareth when we were growing up," he said. He denied that Mary had been a girlfriend of Jesus's, as has been claimed by the 'Spleen Scene' gossip column in the *Moon* tabloid.

Mary said: "We are just very close friends." She dismissed suggestions that Jesus was dour and humourless with a tendency to condemn. "Now that's a joke," said Martha, "God if they only knew him." She called her brother, who had gone inside the house. "Lazarus, Lazarus," she called, "tell the story about the wedding."

Lazarus explained that he and Jesus had been invited to a wedding in Cana. Mark, a man who trained as a carpenter with Jesus and Joseph, was getting married. "Now this fellow Mark was a notorious prankster," explained Lazarus about the bridegroom. "Unknown to me he once nailed a corner of my clothes to a bench they were working on as I was leaving the workshop in Nazareth. I was nearly naked before I realised what he had done."

"Another time he buried money belonging to Jesus, for

a joke. It was never found again because he couldn't remember where he put it. So we had to do something," he said.

What they did was hide most of the wedding wine. Very soon there was none left and the bridegroom was pink with embarrassment as guests wondered why their host was being so mean. "Ye are behind this," said a desperate Mark to them. "Please, fellas. Stop messing," pleaded Mark. But he knew it was hopeless.

So he went to Mary, Jesus's mother. She came outside to where her son was laughing with Lazarus. "Jesus!," she called, "they have no more wine."

"What has this to do with me, Mom? Why are you telling me this?" Jesus said. She turned to staff at the inn and said: "Do whatever he tells ye."

There were six stone jars nearby, which were sometimes used by the Jews for ceremonial washing. He asked the staff to top up each jar with water, then to take some of it to the best man. They did. The best man thought it the best wine he had ever tasted.

He called for Mark. "Everyone else brings out the best wine first and then the cheap wine when people are tipsy. But you, of course, have to do the opposite. Where Mark is concerned the unexpected always happens," he told the guests. And everyone laughed and clapped.

Later people said Jesus had changed the water into wine at Cana. "Now that's the best joke of all," said Lazarus.

Water, wine and a sense of humour
The events in Cana are referred to in Jn 2:1–11.

MISSING PREACHER
FOUND ALIVE AND WELL IN DESERT

JERUSALEM, 30 AD

Stories in the city that the missing preacher Jesus has been seen alive and well have been corroborated by a young man just returned from the Judaean desert. Joseph is a member of a wealthy land-owning family, originally from the Arimathea area. He explained that he was crossing the desert last week when he saw a figure sitting alone on an outcrop of rocks.

Thinking it might be someone in trouble he went towards the man and as he approached recognised him as Jesus. He had seen the preacher in Capernaum and had listened to him there. He was impressed both by what Jesus had said and the natural authority with which he said it. He also liked his courage in attacking the religious authorities and recalled predicting at the time that if Jesus survived the anger of the authorities he would go far.

In the desert, as he came nearer, he asked: "Are you OK?" Jesus said he was fine. It emerged the preacher had been praying and fasting for almost five weeks and planned continuing to do so for at least one more week.

"Forty days and 40 nights," calculated Joseph. "You are a good man." "Why do you call me good?" replied Jesus, "no one is good except God." Then Joseph asked him "What must I do to gain eternal life?"

"You know very well what to do," said Jesus, but he elaborated anyhow. "Keep the commandments. Don't murder. Don't steal. Don't lie. Don't commit adultery. Don't defraud anyone. Treat your parents with respect." Joseph said he had been abiding by all those things since he was a child.

"There is one more thing you must do," said Jesus. "Sell everything you have and give the proceeds to the poor. After that? Follow me. Then you'll have wealth in heaven." Joseph said he had been taken by surprise. He felt he couldn't do this. He liked being wealthy.

"I've bread here if you want some," he said to Jesus. "Get behind me Satan," retorted Jesus angrily, who thought Joseph was trying to tempt him to break his fast. "Man does not live by bread alone," he added, pointedly.

Joseph said he pondered then. "I could help you rule over all Palestine. I could make you ruler even further afield. I would help you get all the power you want and a lifestyle to match. I have the means and I would finance your campaign. That is, of course, if your policies are the same as mine."

Jesus did not conceal his disgust. "My only master is God and he is the only one I serve ... or will serve," he said. Joseph said he then became angry. Contemptuously he said to Jesus: "If you are the 'son of God', as you say you are, throw yourself off these rocks and see what happens. Was it not predicted by the prophets that God would command the angels to protect his son? 'They will lift you in their hands so that you won't even hit your foot on a stone.' Is that not what they said?" he asked.

"They also said that God was not to be tested," Jesus replied. Then, with mock sympathy, he said: "How hard it is to be rich!" Seeing Joseph react with a smile, he continued: "You know it is easier for a camel to go through the eye of a needle than for a rich man to get into heaven."

Joseph told Jesus he was amazed at what he said. "If that's the case everyone is lost … if everyone has to give up what they have, what hope is there for anyone?" he asked. Jesus looked at him directly and said: "It might seem impossible to men but it is not impossible to God. All things are possible with God. And I'll tell you further, no one who has left home or family—brothers, sisters, father, mother, children, even fields—for my sake and what I preach will fail to receive less than a hundred times as much back, in this life and in the next. However, many of those among the first to do so will be last and many who are last will be first."

Joseph said he did not quite understand what this last sentence meant but disregarded it in his overall gloom at what the preacher said. He knew he could never make the sacrifices asked of him, he said. He left Jesus and continued on his journey to Jerusalem.

He said last night he had not been serious in offering to help Jesus become ruler. "I was just testing him," he said, "to see whether he was genuine."

Missing preacher found alive and well in desert
Accounts of the trials of Jesus in the desert are found in Mt 4:1–11; Mk 1:12–13 and Lk 4:1–13. For reference to Joseph of Arimathea, see Jn 19:41.

ATTEMPT TO KILL PREACHER FAILS
IN HOME TOWN

NAZARETH, 30 AD

An attempt to kill the preacher Jesus in his home town, Nazareth, failed this week when he escaped a local mob who tried to throw him from a cliff. One man, who asked not to be named, said Jesus "had it coming to him. He was a grand young fellow, but he's changed lately. Not himself at all."

Another man, who also asked not to be named, said the preacher was "out of his mind. I know the family well. They always thought they were that bit better than everyone else. I mean I heard Joseph (Jesus's step-father) himself say they were descended from King David. But claiming royal blood is one thing, claiming to be the Son of God ... now that's going a bit too far," he said. "There's notions for you!"

Jesus, who had spent the past six weeks praying and fasting in the Judaean desert, suddenly arrived in Nazareth earlier this week. On the Sabbath he went into the synagogue and read to the people from Isaiah: "The spirit of the Lord is on me, because he has anointed me to preach good news to the poor. He has sent me to proclaim freedom for prisoners and recovery of sight for the blind, to release the oppressed, to proclaim the year of the Lord's favour."

Then he rolled up the scroll and said to the people: "Today this scripture is fulfiled in your hearing." They were amazed. "He's claiming to be the Messiah," shouted one woman. "The lunatic!" shouted another. "Isn't this Joseph's lad?" asked one man, laughing. Jesus rose to leave.

"No prophet is ever accepted in his home town," he said, and referred to the experiences of the prophets Elijah and Elisha. This made the people even more angry. "You're no prophet, you're a bloody carpenter," shouted someone at him.

Men in the crowd grabbed Jesus and dragged him out of the synagogue to the top of a cliff above the town. They intended throwing him from it but he managed to escape. He was last seen heading east for Capernaum, near the Lake of Galilee.

Last night, Joseph said he didn't know "what has come over our young fella at all. He's gone that way lately." His eldest (step-)brother, James, said Jesus had "lost the run of himself altogether". He hoped what had happened this week would bring him to his senses.

Mary, Jesus's mother, would not comment at all. However, she did say to Joseph and James, in front of this reporter, that they didn't know what they were talking about, before leaving the company. An embarrassed Joseph commented: "Mothers and sons ... you know the way it is."

Nazareth is a small, nondescript town of about 150 people, built around a spring and encircled by hills on all sides.

Jesus's mother, Mary, lives there with her husband Joseph and their other children, James, Joseph, Judas, Simon, Miriam and Salomé. The latter are Joseph's children from a previous marriage. He was a widower when he married Mary over 30 years ago. Jesus is her only child.

Joseph is a carpenter by trade, as is Jesus, whom he is also said to have trained as a masterbuilder. One of the local men spoken to last night, illustrating the mischievous and popular youngster Jesus had been when he was growing up, recalled how at 12 he went to Jerusalem with Mary and Joseph, to visit the Temple. It was still being built at the time.

"He went missing and they couldn't find him for three days. Mary was in flitters. And there he was in the Temple all the time talking to priests and the builders. 'Did you not know I would be about my father's work?' he said to Mary when she chastised him. An awful ticket. You couldn't keep him out of Joseph's workshop at the time. And he could build anything. I'll tell you how good he was … When they wanted someone to build scenery for a play in Sepphoris (a town nearby)—one of them Greek things—they came to him. Oh, a bright young fellow. It's an awful pity."

His companion blamed the Baptist John. "He was fine until they met. They're cousins, you know. Probably the same notions as well, but there was never any sign of them in Jesus until he met John," he said. "I suppose they must have been there all the time though."

Attempt to kill preacher fails in home town
See Mk 6:1–6; Lk 4:14–30. For an account of the hidden life of the young Jesus and of how he went missing see Lk 1:26–2:50.

TOP JOURNALIST
QUITS JOB TO JOIN JESUS

JERUSALEM, 30 AD

The split between the preacher Jesus and his family deepened this week following a visit by his mother and brothers to Capernaum where he is staying. The attempted reconciliation followed his rejection in Nazareth, where a mob tried to kill him last week.

Since then he has been staying with his friends Peter and Andrew at their home in Capernaum. He was with a group in their house on Tuesday when Peter's mother-in-law, Anna, told him, "Your mother and brothers are outside looking for you."

Jesus refused to meet them. "Ah Jesus," said Peter, "you can't leave them waiting there like that. They're your mother and brothers after all." But Jesus would not move. "Who are my mother and brothers?" he asked. There was no answer. He gestured to the group and said: "Here are my mother and my brothers! Whoever does God's will is my brother and sister and mother." His family left shortly afterwards for Nazareth.

Later, when Jesus was out of earshot, Peter is believed to have advised the others: "Say nothing. Let him cool off. They gave him a rough time last week. It'll be all right. Just wait a bit," he said.

A spokesman for the High Priest Dr Caiaphas said last night the incident "simply highlights the hypocrisy of this man who sees so much hypocrisy in others. How can he talk about love when he treats his own family like that? It seems to me Jesus is about to be found out."

Later in the week the same spokesman expressed surprise on hearing that Mr Judas Iscariot, a journalist with the *Palestinian Times*, had quit his job to help Jesus.

Mr Iscariot is a member of one of Palestine's best-known families. His father, Simon, is one of the leading money-changers in the Temple while his uncle, James, is head of the legal firm, Iscariot and Iscariot, which has offices throughout the country.

Mr Iscariot's decision to join the Jesus campaign also provoked some scepticism. A former colleague said "there must be money in it", and was perplexed Mr Iscariot should think "a penniless, preacher from the back of the beyonds has any future".

Others speculated that the reason was political. The Iscariots are known to be anxious to see the country free of Romans. It has been suggested (primarily by the religious leadership in Jerusalem) that the Jesus campaign, though "dressed up" as religious, is in fact a Trojan horse aimed at the overthrow of Roman rule.

Mr Iscariot's decision has also generated disquiet among Jesus's friends. Sources indicate it caused another row between Peter and John, both of whom claim to be closest to Jesus.

Jesus himself has been visiting friends in Bethany since Wednesday, but it is understood that, in Peter's house on Thursday, John said they should not allow Judas join the group. "He's a journalist," he said, "and there isn't one of those fellows who wouldn't sell his mother for a story. They can't be trusted."

Peter, who recently employed the Iscariot and Iscariot (Capernaum) Ltd legal firm in successful libel proceedings against this column, disagreed. "The Iscariots have connections everywhere and that can only help Jesus. Besides, journalists are God's children too," he said.

Peter then explained that articles by Mr Iscariot about the religious leadership in Jerusalem had been publicly condemned by them as "scurrilous". The articles concerned the leadership's refusal to take a firm stance, one way or another, on the refusal of a rabbi in Galilee to turn away from his synagogue people some considered unclean.

"What more proof do we need? The priests in Jerusalem attack him. He must be alright," Peter said.

It is understood Mr Iscariot has since joined the group.

Top journalist quits job to join Jesus
Compare with Mk 3:20–21; Mk 3:31–35; Lk 6:13–16.

TEMPLE RIOT AVERTED
AFTER ATTACK ON STALLHOLDERS

JERUSALEM, 30 AD

A riot was narrowly averted at the Temple last night when the preacher Jesus threatened and attempted to assault a number of people.

As is usual at this time of year, with preparations for Passover well under way, men were selling cattle, sheep, and doves in the temple grounds for sacrifices to mark the feast while money-changers' stalls were lined along the western wall to exchange coins as only those without an image can be donated to the Temple. It is the custom that no coins bearing the image of Caesar or anyone else are donated.

Jesus became enraged. He made a whip out of cords and began to roar and scream and flailed the men about him until they ran off.

He shouted at dove sellers: "Get these out of here! How dare ye turn my father's house into a market!" They ran, terrified. Witnesses said the preacher was actually frothing at the mouth.

At a distance from the Temple, the sellers regrouped and began to get angry themselves. Mr Simon Iscariot was heard to say: "Who the hell does this fella think he is?" Mr Iscariot owns most of the money-changing stalls in the Temple. Others expressed similar sentiments. They then returned to the Temple en masse to confront Jesus.

"Who do you think you are? What gives you the authority to behave like this? Show us ... show us ... what gives you the right?" they shouted at him. Jesus stared back at them and replied: "Destroy this temple and I will raise it again in three days."

Mr Iscariot muttered to the others: "This guy's a looper." He turned to Jesus and said: "It has taken 46 years to build this Temple and you are going to raise it in three days? Are you crazy?"

Jesus ignored him and walked through the crowd out of the Temple area. They stood aside as he still held the whip.

The incident has caused uproar in the city. The Roman authorities ordered the preacher's immediate arrest for disturbing the peace, a serious charge at this time of the year when Jerusalem is full of pilgrims. A spokesman for the Governor, Mr Pilate, said Jesus could have caused a major riot.

Soldiers went to the home of Lazarus, at Bethany near the city, where it was reported Jesus had been staying. But he had left. Lazarus has since lodged a formal complaint against the soldiers, alleging they ransacked his house and threatened his sisters Martha and Mary. It is not known where Jesus is at the moment.

A spokesman for the High Priest, Dr Caiaphas, demanded that "real" action be taken against the preacher. "Sooner or later someone will die if this fellow is allowed carry on with his antics. He works up simple, uneducated people into a frenzy and channels their manufactured hatred against our rulers and our religious leadership generally. And now he does this! It simply cannot be allowed to continue. Then you have his cousin John stirring up people against King Herod.

The two of them must be dealt with, and soon. Otherwise we are all in trouble," he said.

Meanwhile, Frank, Environment Correspondent of the *Palestinian Times*, dismissed Jesus's claims about rebuilding the Temple in three days as "the outpourings of a diseased mind". He said: "Desirable and all as it would be to level that monstrosity it would take far more than three days to do it, never mind rebuild it. And it should not be rebuilt."

But he commended Jesus for clearing the temple area, where he now lives himself. He complained that "all sorts of undesirables—and some far worse than this Jesus fellow—have been crowding into the area recently. Whipping is too good them. Something really has to be done," he said.

APOLOGY

This publication dissociates itself completely from a suggestion, quoted in a previous Report, that Mr Judas Iscariot was motivated by money in his decision to join the Jesus campaign.

We accept this is totally untrue and that Mr Iscariot is a man of the highest integrity and noblest aspiration, and we deeply regret any offence caused.

Following discussions with solicitors Iscariot and Iscariot (Capernaum) Ltd we have agreed to pay Mr Iscariot a significant sum of money as compensation.

An offer to pay the amount to a charity was declined.

Temple riot averted after attack on stallholders
Look at Mt 21:12–17; Mk 11:15–19 and Lk 19:45–48.
John gives a different perspective at Jn 2:13–25.

"Pudsy has lost run of himself," says Salomé

Jerusalem, 30 AD

Considerable offence was caused to some devout Jews by an article in the *Palestinian Times* last Tuesday, titled "Considering the Moses of fact and faith". It dealt with questions raised by scholars as to the authenticity of stories surrounding the prophet and included such lines as: "He was not found in a basket, nor was it in the Nile, nor was it by Pharaoh's daughter. There was no 'slavery in Egypt', no 'burning bush', no tablets of stone, nor were the Ten Commandments written."

Written by "Pudsy", hitherto unknown and of suspect belief, it continued that the greater part of the four books covering Moses's life—Exodus, Leviticus, Numbers and Deuteronomy—was "literary creation", while just 18 per cent of the words attributed to him in them may actually have been said by him at all.

The article went on to quote Dermot, a highly-respected rabbi, as saying these views were "not by any means original". The four books, he said, were a blend of fact, story and historical interpretation "as is every document, including *Palestinian Times* editorials". There was, moreover, no such thing as the notion of detached, historical objectivity, because "he who selects interprets".

But what he felt most significant about the controversy surrounding Moses was "the deep fascination with the person of Moses by believers and unbelievers alike".

Some people, however, remained angered that such sceptical views should be printed at all, and just a day before Passover began. Pudsy was denounced by Jews-in-the-street for "crass insensitivity" and "deliberate provocation".

A young woman named Salomé wrote to him that "greater minds than yours have tried to deny the books of Moses in the 1,250 years since they were written and have failed. You also will fail. You are taking on the might and power of the living and true God, who will not be denied. The Creator of everything that exists has defeated more powerful enemies than Pudsy." Pudsy has not responded and, it is believed, may have fled to the Judaean desert.

Meanwhile, the city has calmed down following the near-riot situation created at the Temple last week when the preacher Jesus went berserk. Sources indicate he is back in Capernaum with his friends, Peter and Andrew. It is understood that at a meeting with his core group there he appointed Judas Iscariot campaign treasurer.

Others among the preacher's core group include Peter and Andrew, the sons of Zebedee James and John, friends Philip and Bartholomew. Then there is Thomas, a man said to be without conviction on most matters and a surprise choice by Jesus.

Another surprise choice was the tax collector, Matthew. He was alleged to have been involved in the "payments-to-(Roman) officials" scandal some years ago. It was claimed that large sums of money were exchanged before a huge site was cleared to enable an extensive courtyard be built around the Temple in Jerusalem. Matthew has always denied the allegations and complained about the effects they have had on himself and his family. "It is very difficult to be frank," he said.

Simon, still referred to as "the Zealot" though he has long since abandoned arms, is another of the core twelve. The remaining two are the comparatively unknown James, son of Alphaeus, and Thaddaeus.

A large number of women are also involved in the campaign. The best known is Mary, from Magdala, a town on the west of Lake Galilee. She is known generally as Mary Magdalene. She is particularly well-known in Jerusalem, where she spent many happy and active years.

She was said to be especially popular in higher social circles and accompanied many prominent personalities to functions at both the Governor's palace and the High Priest's residence. She left Jerusalem some time ago and has been living in Galilee since. It was there she first became aware of Jesus. She is now among his most loyal supporters and is considered to be a major asset to his campaign.

"Pudsy has lost run of himself," says Salomé
For the call of the apostles, see Mt 4:18–22; Mt 9:9; Mt 10:1–16; Mk 1:16–20; Mk 2:13–14; Mk 3:13–19; Lk 6:13–16; Lk 5:27–28. For names of the women who followed Jesus, see Lk 8:1–3.

ANIMAL RIGHTS ACTIVISTS
THREATEN THE PALE GALILEAN

CAPERNAUM, 31 AD

The preacher Jesus has been speaking in the towns and villages of the Galilee and Decapolis provinces all week and once more large crowds follow him wherever he goes. Many cures are again being attributed to him by people desperate for good health.

He has been deeply moved by the suffering he encountered and was overheard at Hippos comparing the people crowding around him to sheep without a shepherd—poor, lost, helpless. "So much to do, so few to do it," he said. He asked people to pray to God to send more help.

Last Wednesday at Gadara in Decapolis he fell foul of farmers and local animal rights activists, who blamed him for the mass slaughter of a herd of pigs. Like lemmings they chased over a cliff and drowned in a lake, below, when he shouted at them. One version of what happened claims Jesus encountered two violent men who had the area terrorised. Because of their irrational behaviour and as they lived in a tomb in the local graveyard—which a lot of homeless people do in Gadara—it was believed they were in league with the devil.

The two demanded of Jesus why he had come to annoy them. He did not answer. Then, as if they had become believers in their own publicity, one of them said: "If you drive me (the devil) out, send me into those pigs there." They indicated a herd nearby. Jesus looked, pronounced a commanding "Go", and the pigs chased off squealing in terror. They ran blind, over the cliff.

Their minders were very, very angry. They went into Gadara and, furiously, told people in the town what had happened. A large angry crowd went out to meet Jesus and asked him to leave the area. Some were concerned about what might happen to their own pigs should he stay, while a younger, more vociferous element demanded he explain how he would dare treat any of God's creatures in such a way.

"This is more of your macho-stuff," one young woman said to him. "What you did to those pigs was every bit as brutal as what you said to that young man here yesterday, when he asked could he bury his father before joining your campaign. 'Let the dead bury the dead' Indeed! Who the hell do you think you are?" She was physically restrained by the crowd. "You'd better get out of here," an older man advised Jesus. And he left.

In a fascinating insight into his campaign strategy, the *Galilee Leader* newspaper carried a detailed report on Friday of a secret meeting held by Jesus with his core campaign group the previous night. At the meeting he had explained to the twelve— "the Jesus 12" as they have become known locally—what they must do to ensure victory.

"Avoid non-Jews and Samaria. Stick with the still floating, non-aligned people in Israel. They're the best hope. Tell them heaven is near. Tell them you'll cure the sick, raise the dead, drive out devils. Don't bother about campaign contributions and don't even worry about the shirt on your back. Whatever town or village it is, stay with a decent supporter for as long as is necessary and you are welcome.

"And if you are not made feel welcome shake the dust of the place off your feet as fast as you can. They will pay dearly for it. I'm sending you out like sheep among wolves. Be as shrewd as snakes and innocent as doves. And if they hassle you and make your life miserable or worse—and they will—don't worry what to say. The words will take care of themselves. Then get out of there as fast as you can.

"Don't ever be afraid. God knows the number of every hair on your head. He will protect you. And remember I am not here to bring peace. Rather I will be the reason why a man will stand against his father, a daughter against her mother. I want total dedication, nothing less will do. And anyone who is good to you will be remembered by me."

The newspaper report has inspired much cynical comment in Capernaum. "A typical politician," said a local fisherman yesterday, "promising heaven on earth. He will cure the sick and raise the dead… How can anyone take these guys seriously? Do they think the people are stupid or what? One thing's for sure. Jesus or no Jesus I'll still be fishing for fish," he said. And he went back to mending his nets.

Animal rights activists threaten the pale Galilean
See Mt 8:28–34; Mk 5:1–20 and Lk 8:26–36. Refer also to
Mt 9:35–37; Mt 10:1–42; Lk 9:1–6; Lk 10:2–16 and Mk 6:7–13.

Protests follow arrest of "the Baptist"

Jerusalem, 31 AD

The arrest of the preacher John has caused a storm of protest both in Jerusalem and throughout the province of Galilee particularly. Known as "the Baptist" because of his practice of pouring water over people to symbolise they have been born again, his arrest took place last night.

It is understood that King Herod had given the order and that John is now being detained at the king's palace where it is reported the preacher has been tied up and is imprisoned. It is not known if John is to be tried or what he is to be charged with.

The consensus among the authorities in Jerusalem is that John had it coming to him. A source close to the High Priest Dr Caiaphas said: "What did he expect? For months and months he has been holding the king and his wife up to public condemnation at worst, ridicule at the very least. It is remarkable he wasn't arrested ages ago."

The source agreed that the marital arrangement between the king and his companion Herodias was not "strictly valid" in the eyes of the religious authorities, "but how do we know what goes on between them? How can we condemn without direct evidence of the nature of their relationship?"

He angrily denied suggestions that, were an ordinary couple involved, the religious authorities would be down on them like a ton of bricks.

He also disagreed with the view that, whatever the reality, by living with his brother's wife the king was giving scandal and that it could encourage other couples to do likewise.

He ended the interview abruptly when it was suggested that John had simply been true to the law of God in condemning the relationship while the religious authorities had remained silent out of cowardice. "That," he said, was "the suggestion of a guttersnipe."

A spokesman for the governor, Mr Pontius Pilate, said the matter was an internal one for the Palestinian authorities in which he had no interest. A source at the governor's residence, however, commented that the arrest was another example of "the primitive level at which these people operate".

He also suggested John's condemnation of the relationship of the king and Herodias was just an indication of "the superstitious nature and general lack of sophistication of these people". He felt the royal relationship itself was no more than "the vulgar get-together of two crass people".

Throughout Galilee, there has been outrage at the arrest, not least among the followers of Jesus, though he himself has said nothing publicly on the matter. Many believe he feels compromised as John is his cousin. His mother, Mary, and John's mother, Elizabeth, are said to be close.

John is an only child and arrived late in the married life of Elizabeth and her husband, the priest Zachariah. Neither expected to have children but—the story goes—while burning incense in the Temple, Zachariah saw a figure to the right of the altar which said to him he would have a son and his name would be John. "He will be a great man, who will bring you much pride and joy. He won't drink but will bring many people back to God," Zachariah would recall later.

But he doubted this and he found he was unable to speak from that day until John was born. People said it was a miracle. Zachariah had a reputation for talking too much and his sudden silence brought peace to many. It ended when the baby boy was born and all the neighbours had gathered around to choose a name. They decided on Zachariah, which surprised no one. But Elizabeth wanted "John", and they were perplexed as there was no John anywhere in that family.

And they made signs to Zachariah to see what he thought. He struggled for speech so he could say the boy must be called John, and eventually scrawled the word "John" on the table top. "John" he said then, and they all looked at him in astonishment. "He's talking," remarked one of the neighbours, without joy.

But Zachariah could not stop praising God and his lovely son and he told them about the man in the Temple and what he had said to him nine months before and how he didn't believe him and that he couldn't speak since and how awful it was not to be able to speak......

Protests follow arrest of "the Baptist"
For these events, look at Mt 14:3–5; Mk 6:14–20; Lk 9:7–9.
For a perspective on John's birth and early life see Lk 1:5–25
and Lk 1:57–80.

Tabloid press falls upon
Mary of Magdala

Jerusalem, 31 AD

Seismic tremors passed through civic and religious circles in the city this week following revelations in the *Palestinian Times* on Tuesday that Mary, now with the Jesus campaign, was part of a "services for votes" scandal in the city about eight years ago.

When confronted by the newspaper Mary, known as Mary Magdalene as she is from the town of Magdala on Lake Galilee, admitted she had worked with the "Hot Stuff" escort agency in the city and that she and other women there had provided services to religious and political figures at the behest of the Scruples building company. It was seeking the contract to extend the Temple courtyard at the time. It won the contract.

Ms Magdalene also supplied the paper with a list of names of those men she had attended to at the time and others she recalled being with her escort colleagues. "Hot Stuff" was disbanded two years ago when the owners were jailed for money laundering. Ms Magdalene left it some years before and has altered her way of life significantly.

The *Palestinian Times* did not publish Ms Magdalene's list and may not be able to do so for legal reasons, but its very existence prompted a flurry of denials from leading religious and political figures. A spokesman for the High Priest, Dr Caiaphas, said that while he had seen Ms Magdalene at functions in his residence he had never been in her company.

A similar statement was released by Governor Pilate. He too acknowledged that Ms Magdalene had been to his palace, but that she was always accompanied by others. A leading judge has been linked in gossip columns with Ms Magdalene, as has a leading centurion.

The well-known critic of the courtyard extension, Mr Isaiah Bunni, also denied ever being with Ms Magdalene, and said the reason he had not been present when a vote was taken on the Temple courtyard extension was because he was pre-occupied with more important business.

The following day, Wednesday, the *Moon* tabloid published on its front page a photograph of Mr Bunni being kissed by Ms Magdalene, under the heading "Bunni Smacked". That afternoon he issued a statement saying that, while Ms Magdalene kissed him, he had not kissed her back. "I am a gentleman," he said, "I will not refuse any woman's kisses."

Meanwhile a lively trade in T-shirts has sprung up in the city because of the controversy. The message on the T-shirts reads: "I did not sleep with Mary Magdalene, either!"

On Thursday, the *Moon* was forced into a front-page apology to Jesus, the preacher. It had reported him the previous day as saying he did not have a sexual relationship with Ms Magdalene. The report continued that when asked what he did for sex, he replied: "Not nearly as much as it does for me."

In its apology the tabloid acknowledged the last remark was not made by Jesus at all, but "may have arisen because the reporter misunderstood what was actually said". It was not reported what Jesus actually said.

In Galilee Jesus continues to be followed by great crowds wherever he goes teaching and preaching, and everywhere people claim he has performed remarkable cures. Words of this reached John "the Baptist", still being detained without charge by King Herod. He sent one of his followers to Galilee to ask Jesus whether he was the one promised by God so long ago or should they go on waiting.

Typically, when this question was put to Jesus by John's follower, he did not answer directly. "Tell John what you see," he said, "the blind see, the lame walk, lepers are cured, the deaf hear, the dead rise, and the good news is preached to the poor."

When John's disciples left, Jesus said to the crowd: "No one born is greater than John but the least person in heaven is greater than him. And still John is not recognised for who he is. What is wrong with these people? He lived in the desert neither eating nor drinking and they said the devil was in him. I eat and drink and they call me a drunkard, a glutton, a friend of the corrupt and depraved, and worse. But truth will out!"

Tabloid press falls upon Mary of Magdala
For Mary of Magdala, look at Lk 8:2 and Mt 11:1–15.

SHOCK AT REPORT OF JOHN'S DEATH IN HEROD'S PALACE

JERUSALEM, 31 AD

There was deep shock in the city at news that the preacher John had been found dead in his cell at King Herod's palace early on Wednesday morning last. A statement from the palace said the preacher, known as "the Baptist", appeared to have died of natural causes but that doctors were conducting an investigation.

The results of the investigation were released on Thursday. It said John had died following a severe heart attack. He had been ill with pains in his chest most of the previous day, it said. Following a request that the body be handed over, friends of John were told it had already been buried in the palace grounds.

"On security advice it was felt this would be in the best interest of public order as the funeral could have become a focus for unruly elements," a palace spokesman said.

John's friends were outraged and appealed to Governor Pilate to intervene. He said it was an internal matter and for King Herod to deal with. An appeal to the High Priest, Dr Caiaphas, was also unsuccessful. He said it was a civic not a religious matter and he had no authority in the area. He expressed "regret" at John's death.

One of John's friends said he believed the preacher had been murdered and that was why the body was not being released. "It's a cover-up," he said, "and I'll get to the bottom of it if it takes the rest of my life. What sort of country are we living in when an innocent man like John can be got rid of like that?" he asked.

The *Moon* tabloid greeted the news with the headline "Gone—Soon Forgotten". It described the preacher as "a barking mad lunatic who should have stayed in the desert where he belonged". It said John was like a cactus "all needles with mush in his head. One preacher gone is good news, but there are too many roaming the country sponging off the people. They should all be deported or jailed."

There has been no response to John's death from the Jesus campaign. Reports indicate that on hearing the news Jesus himself withdrew into the desert on his own for a day. Others said this was because of an incident near Capernaum.

There Jesus saw a mob stoning a man who was believed to have sexually abused children. He shouted at them to stop and they stood back. He rested his hand on the kneeling man's injured head and challenged the mob angrily. "If there is a man among you and he has never done anything seriously wrong in his life let him step forward. He can throw the first stone!"

"Come on ... I'm waiting," he shouted. The crowd began to mutter. Someone shouted "paedophile lover" at Jesus. Someone else roared. "You're another bloody pervert. All ye preachers are the same. Twisted bastards." But no one stepped forward. The atmosphere was tense.

The man who was being stoned looked up at Jesus and said, "You'd better go. There's no point in the two of us being killed and I deserve it." Jesus said nothing. He stayed put. The mob began to disperse eventually, shouting back obscenities.

He helped the man to his feet. "Now, go and sin no more," he said to him. The man was profuse with gratitude and was beginning to be a nuisance when one of Jesus's friends said, "Will you go while you can, before that crowd come back." And he went.

Judas Iscariot was said to have been infuriated at the incident. An unconfirmed report said he and Jesus had a stand-up row there on the side of the road. He is said to have told Jesus he was ruining the campaign. "Whores, adulterers, paedophiles, tax collectors, drunks lepers … look at the company you keep? How in God's name do you hope to get anywhere hanging around with those sort of people? And they say paedophiles are incurable …"

"So are lepers." Jesus is reported to have replied. "We must separate the person from the disease. We must cherish the person whatever the disease," he was reported as saying. Judas was then said to have pleaded with Jesus to stop fraternising with such company. "We'll soon run out of funds," he is believed to have said, "and I can't run a campaign without money."

"So?" Jesus is said to have replied. And Judas is supposed to have stormed off.

Shock at report of John's death in Herod's palace
For John's death, look at Mt 14:3–12; Mk 6:17–29.

JUDAS OUTLINES STRATEGY
TO DEAL WITH BAD PRESS

JERUSALEM, 31 AD

A report in this week's edition of the *Galilee News* has sparked a bitter dispute between the local newspaper and Mr Judas Iscariot, treasurer of the Jesus campaign. Of late Mr Iscariot has also been playing a leading role in publicity for the campaign. In that context, he addressed a meeting of the core campaign group on Monday.

Jesus was absent. It was said he has withdrawn to a solitary place as news of the death of John, and the rumours surrounding it, began to sink in.

At the meeting, which was attended by a reporter from the *Galilee News,* though few present seemed aware of that, Mr Iscariot outlined a strategy for dealing with bad publicity. He has become concerned that some actions of Jesus, as well as the company he keeps, is dragging the campaign down, he said.

He spoke "as a former journalist; one who understands the mind-set of these people", and outlined a six-point plan for "rubbishing" bad publicity.

"Remember that the truth or otherwise of a story is not important, what you must do is get the public to believe your version of events. It is not the truth but the public's perception of what is true that matters. It is essential therefore, especially if what was written is true, that you undermine the credibility of the reporter involved.

"1. Ignore the substantive truth of the story and pick on an inaccurate detail. You will always find one. Reporters deal with immense amounts of information which must be reduced to a few broad points and in very limited time. They tend therefore to generalise, and all generalisations are dangerous. Even this one!

"2. An alternative strategy is to suggest ignorance on the part of the reporter. Propose he/she misunderstood/ misrepresented/did not realise/recognise the context of what was being said.

"3. Regardless of which strategy you adopt, or both, it is essential you appear mad with rage. Ring the reporter and berate him/her. Ring the editor and berate him/her.   Use key words like 'appalling', 'outrageous', 'scurillous', 'unbelievable' and semi-flattering phrases such as 'I cannot believe a paper of your standard could be so shoddy/ careless/reckless etc. etc.'

"Make plenty of noise. That way they begin to doubt themselves. Besides, the reporter and editor are already many stories away from your one and are dealing with further immense amounts of information. They will want to be rid of you. They don't need the hassle. Make yourself enough of a pain and they will soon agree to almost anything.

"4. Mention law and any hesitation on their part will go out the window.

"5. Insist the reporter be named in the apology/ correction. That will keep him/her in line in any future dealings with you.

"6. Never let a hint of this tactic come to their attention

or they will go after you tooth and nail until you're well and truly finished."

This was not received well by Jesus's friends. Peter said, "You are asking us to lie?" John said, "Jesus would never agree to this." Andrew said he didn't think Mr Iscariot should be with the campaign at all. Mr Iscariot advised them to "please, please come into the real world". The others would not agree. "This is the very sort of thing Jesus is trying to stop," said Peter.

When the report appeared in the *Galilee News*, Mr Iscariot rang the reporter and his editor and remonstrated with them angrily. It is understood the newspaper has been unsuccessful so far in getting comment from any of Jesus's friends on the matter. The editor, Mr Aeolus, said last night an apology was being considered for next week's edition.

APOLOGY

We deeply regret that Patsy McGarry repeated scurrilous and wholly false rumours about the recent death of the preacher John in a previous Jesus Report. We are entirely confident John died of natural causes, as explained by King Herod and confirmed later by doctors at the palace. As a token of our regret we have made a substantial financial contribution towards the further education in dance of Ms Salomé, the king's step-daughter. It is widely agreed she has a most exquisite talent.

EXCITABLE PETER GOES OVERBOARD

LAKE GALILEE, 31 AD

Environmentalists held a protest here this week at the littering of nearby hills by crowds following the preacher Jesus. He was thought to be staying with his friends Lazarus, Martha, and Mary in Bethany, but he was found last Tuesday on a hill near Lake Galilee. He was in deep mourning for his cousin John.

Thousands of people climbed the hillside. He wanted to be alone, but when he saw their sufferings he felt great pity and healed them. The more he healed the more came to him.

As evening approached, some of his friends became concerned that people would find nothing to eat. "This is a remote place and it's late. Send them to the villages so they can buy themselves something to eat," they said.

Jesus took no heed and—not for the first time—they were annoyed with him. "He's impossible," they muttered. "How can he be so careless, so irresponsible?"

"They don't need to go away. Give them something to eat," Jesus said to them. They thought—and not for the first time—that he had lost the run of himself.

"For God's sake, look," they responded, "all we have are five loaves and two fish and there must be 5,000 people here." Jesus was unperturbed. "Bring them here," he said. He told the crowd to sit on the grass. Then he took the loaves and fish and looked up to heaven. He prayed. He appeared to make a blessing and broke the loaves with his hands.

He called his friends and told them to break the loaves

and hand out the bread. "There's hardly enough here for five, never mind 5,000," said Thomas, "… it's impossible!" Peter said: "For once in your life, Thomas, will you just do something without telling us it's impossible." And he did.

Everyone ate as much fish and bread as they wanted and Jesus's friends picked up what was left. In all, 12 baskets were collected. Unfortunately they were dumped not too far from Capernaum and began to attract vermin.

It was that which led to local environmentalists organising a public meeting in Capernaum to protest at what one speaker described as "this outrageous attempt to create a landfill site so near our town". Jesus and his friends were condemned by all for attracting such crowds to the area, leaving the litter now defacing the countryside. There were calls for the Jesus campaign to be banned. Reports of his miracles were dismissed as "trickery".

When a speaker from the crowd said Jesus had fed 5,000 people with five loaves and two fish it too was dismissed as trickery. A local rabbi asked: "Do you really believe all those people went to such a remote place without bringing any food with them? They're not stupid in Galilee. But some people are prepared to believe anything about this Jesus character. Next thing they'll be telling us he can walk on water."

The next day it was reported that Jesus had walked on water. During the night some of his friends were in a boat on the lake when a storm blew up and they thought they would drown. Then they saw Jesus coming to them walking on the water and they didn't know which was most terrifying, imminent death or an encounter with what they thought was a ghost.

"Will ye have a bit of courage. Don't be afraid. It's only me," said Jesus. And, assured it was him, they were wildly excited. Peter got carried away. "If it's yourself, Jesus, then ask me to join you on the water," he said. "Come on then," said Jesus. As soon as he tried Peter's bravado began to evaporate. He walked on the water a bit, then got frightened and started to sink. He roared at Jesus, "Save me, save me."

Jesus took Peter's hand and, laughing, said: "O you of little faith." Then, seriously, he asked: "Why did you doubt?" Peter had no answer. The others were amazed. "There's no doubt about it, he's the son of God," said one of them. They landed at Gennesaret.

When the rabbi in Capernaum heard the story about Jesus walking on water he said to a crowd gleefully: "Forgive me, please forgive me, for what I am about to say but … I told you so!"

* The *Galilee News* has apologised to Mr Judas Iscariot for "the glaringly inaccurate report" of his talk on dealing with bad publicity in the previous Report.

Excitable Peter goes overboard
For the miracle of the loaves see Mt 14:13–21 and Mt 15:32–39; Mk 6:30–56 and Mk 8:1–10; and also Jn 6:1–14. With regard to the walking on water see Mk 4:35–41; Mk 6:45–52; Mt 14:22–36 and Jn 6:15–21.

MANY TURNED OFF BY MESSAGE OF JESUS

CAPERNAUM, 31 AD
Support for the Jesus campaign collapsed this week following an extraordinary speech by the preacher in the synagogue at Capernaum on Wednesday. He was heckled and handclapped before some people, mainly women, led a mass walk-out.

"How do we do what God wants?" he was asked. "Believe in who he has sent," said Jesus. Some in the crowd muttered darkly at what was considered to be an outrageous claim. "How can you prove this?" a woman asked.

"The bread of God is he who has come down from heaven and gives life to the world," Jesus said. Everyone was confused.

"Why can't he talk plain like everyone else?" wondered one man.

"I am the bread of life. Anyone who comes to me will never be hungry. Anyone who believes in me will never be thirsty. And whoever comes to me will never be turned away. You have all seen what I can do and still you don't believe in me.

"I have come down from heaven to do the will of him who sent me. Not my will. Everyone who believes in his son I will raise up on the last day," Jesus said.

There was uproar. "He thinks he is the son of God," shouted a man above the boos and jeers. "Isn't he the son of that carpenter Joseph?"

Another said: "Don't we all know his seed, breed and generation? And the likes of him now tells us he came from heaven … for the love of God!"

Jesus declared: "I tell ye whoever believes in me will live forever." "Lunatic," shouted a voice from the crowd. "Go back to where you came from," roared another. But he continued: "I am the bread of life. Your forefathers ate manna and still they died. But I am the living bread that came from heaven. Anyone who eats this bread will live forever. This bread is my flesh. I will give it for the world."

"He wants to turn us into cannibals," shouted someone in the crowd.

"I tell you unless you eat the flesh of the son of man and drink his blood, you will have no life in you," Jesus told them.

"Outrageous", "disgusting", "blasphemy …" were among the responses as the crowd began to walk out. "Whoever eats my flesh and drinks my blood will live forever and I'll raise them on the last day … they remain in me and I in them." Soon the synagogue was nearly empty.

"Who can believe this sort of thing?" asked a man who stayed on.

"Why does it upset you?" Jesus replied. "Suppose you saw the son of man ascend to where he came from. What then? The Spirit is what matters. The flesh is nothing. What I have been saying is spirit. And still … even you, some of you, don't believe."

Soon only the core twelve were left.

"Do ye want to go too?" Jesus asked. Peter replied: "Where would we go? You have the words that will live

forever. We believe in you. That you are the holy one of God."
But Jesus seemed unconvinced.

"Have I not chosen ye?" he asked, "… yet one of you
will betray me." There was deep shock at this remark.

A source close to the twelve felt it must refer to either
Peter or John.

Peter, it was said, was unreliable. While John, it was
said, was "unhealthily close" to Jesus. Lately he has been
referring to himself as "the beloved disciple". There are fears
of sad consequences if the friendship should sour. So it was
said.

A suggestion that the reference might be to Judas was
dismissed out of hand. Mr Iscariot, it was said, is seen as "one
of Jesus's most valued and trusted friends".

Regardless, informed opinion in Palestine is firmly of
the view that the Jesus campaign is now well and truly
finished. "In sæcula sæculorum" (forever and ever), as the
Romans say—as one source put it.

Many turned off by message of Jesus
For the discourse covered in this Report, see Jn 6:22–71.

JUDAS ISCARIOT
HOSTS A BIZARRE PRESS BRIEFING

CAPERNAUM, 31 AD

If there was any doubt about the desperation besetting the Jesus campaign it was dispelled at a bizarre press conference in Capernaum this week. It took place at the home of Peter and Andrew, headquarters of the campaign, and without Jesus himself. Which was a bit like *Antigone* without the princess.

Conducted by Mr Judas Iscariot, effectively spin doctor supreme of the campaign, it featured a rabbi and his daughter, a Roman centurion, a waiter from Cana, a previously deaf and mute man who could not be silent, a young boy of about seven, and a nervous older woman.

Mr Iscariot apologised for the absence of Jesus, explaining he was visiting a sick friend. This was a reference to Lazarus in Bethany, who has not been well lately. It emerged since that Jesus was opposed to the press conference, saying it was not what he is about. It went ahead at Mr Iscariot's insistence.

Mr Iscariot conceded that Jesus's "I am the bread of life" speech in Capernaum last week had not been well received, but said it had been misunderstood. Jesus had not been speaking literally, he said. "He was explaining something complicated in a simple way, like he does with parables," he said.

He introduced the people referred to above, each of whom had a tale to tell of the wonderful things Jesus had done for them. The rabbi Jairus said, "He raised my little girl from the dead," patting his smiling daughter on the head. The reporters laughed.

"They laughed then, too," said Jairus. "I told him my little girl had died and he said she was not dead, just sleeping, and the crowd around us laughed just like you. Well, here she is," he said.

The nervous woman intervened. "He was on his way to Rabbi Jairus's house when I saw him. I had this bleeding disorder for 12 years, as long as that little girl is alive. I touched his cloak and I was cured straight away."

"… And I was born deaf and could not speak," said the talkative man. "He put his fingers into my ears. He spat and touched my tongue with his spittle. He looked to heaven and said, 'Be opened.' And I could hear and I could speak. You have no idea how wonderful it feels."

Mr Iscariot turned to the Roman. "And you, sir, you're a stranger here. What did he do for you?" The centurion, who was a well-liked man said: "My best servant was very sick. I had heard great things about Jesus. I went to him and told him just to say the words and my servant would be all right. And he did. My man hasn't looked back since."

"And what did he do for you, little boy?" asked Mr Iscariot of the seven-year-old. "I don't know, sir," he replied. Which was a relief from the by now leaden parade of wonders. Everyone laughed. "Weren't you possessed by an evil spirit and didn't it make you roll around and foam at the mouth, grinding your teeth and then go stiff?" And the boy asked. "Did it, sir?" to the delight of the media present who enjoy nothing more than seeing the best-laid plans of spin doctors explode in their faces.

The boy's father stood up. He said: "It was like that and had been for years. Even these men here, Peter, John, Andrew, none of them could do anything. I begged Jesus. He said to the spirit in my boy, 'Come out of him and never enter him again.'

"My lad was thrown about the place shouting and roaring and then lay like a corpse. I was sure he was dead. Jesus took him by the hand and lifted him to his feet and he was as good as you see him there now."

The waiter from Cana was asked why he was there. "I can prove he turned water into wine," he said. "I was there." He had heard the story that it was a prank by Jesus and Lazarus ... "But I know it was water," he insisted.

Asked how he knew, he became embarrassed. "We usually 'sample' the wine beforehand," he said, "and I can tell you for certain there was just water in those jars before Jesus got to work on them. There's no doubt about it."

Judas Iscariot hosts a bizarre press briefing
For the daughter of Jairus and the woman with a bleeding disorder see Mt 9:18–26; Mk 5:22–43; Lk 8: 40–56; for the deaf and dumb man, Mk 7:31–37; for the centurion's servant Mt 8:5–13, Lk 7:1–10 (and look also at Jn 4:46–54); for the boy cured by Jesus where the disciples had failed, see Mt 17:14–21; Mk 9:16–28; Lk 9:37–43; for the Cana waiter's story see Jn 2:1–11.

Palace rocked
as Salomé gives her story to the press

Jerusalem, 31 AD

It has been a week of unprecedented crisis and one which has seriously threatened the rule of King Herod. It followed an interview with Salomé, the king's stepdaughter, published in the *Palestinian Times* on Monday.

She claimed the preacher John, known as 'the Baptist', had been beheaded last month by order of the king. A palace spokesman had said at the time that John had died of natural causes. Ms Salomé also claimed the beheading had been at her mother's instigation.

It is believed that John had been arrested because of his relentless condemnations of the king's marriage to Herodias, Salomé's mother.

Herodias had been married to the king's brother, Prince Philip. She was particularly incensed by John's criticisms but King Herod, who admired the preacher, refused to have him killed at the time. Salomé said this had made her mother very angry.

On the king's birthday last month there was a banquet at the palace. Salomé, who is a very talented dancer, performed after the meal and everyone was greatly impressed.

"Ask me for whatever you want and you can have it ...," the proud king said to her as his guests applauded, "... anything you want!" Salomé didn't know what to ask for. Her mother said: "Ask for John's head ... on a platter!" And she did.

There was a shocked silence in the banqueting hall. Salomé told the *Palestinian Times* it was then she realised the enormity of what she had done. But it was too late. The request had been made. King Herod was upset, she said, but felt he could not refuse her. He called for the deed to be done.

The subsequent moments were the longest of her life, she said. "Everything was ruined. Everyone just stared at me. I used be a favourite with these people but looking around I could see this was no longer the case. I wanted to be anywhere else."

The executioner soon arrived back with John's dripping, bloody, open-eyed head on a platter. Some of the guests were sick and had to leave the room. The king was pale. Herodias smiled.

A spokesman for the palace dismissed Salomé's story as "hysterical nonsense". He said she was being treated by doctors at the palace for months because she "suffered disturbances". This failed to reassure the public. There were calls for the release of John's body.

"Show us the body," demanded the preacher's friends. The palace had said at the time that John was buried in the grounds there to avoid likely public disorder at his funeral.

John's friends petitioned the Governor, Pilate, to have the body released. He said that it was an internal matter. But it is known he made strong representations behind the scenes.

The palace resisted. Herodias told reporters that her life had been hell because of rumours since John died. The king, her husband, was the most decent man she had ever known and it was grossly unfair to make her family suffer in that way, she said.

In interviews with selected reporters the king said he had done nothing wrong. He and his associates at court had always worked to help people, and as a team, he said. They had been accessible, not aloof. "This is not an ivory tower," he was quoted as saying.

"Show us the body," demanded John's friends.

On Friday evening the palace issued a terse statement saying John had indeed been beheaded but that it had been "a mistake". Another prisoner had been sentenced to death for murder and the executioner had been misinformed as to who was sentenced, it said. The executioner had himself since been put to death for his error, it continued.

"Then, following careful reflection and acting solely in the best interests of public order, it was felt that John's body should not be released, or details of his death. We deeply regret this decision but it cannot be undone. We wish to express our deepest sympathy to the relatives and friends of this man who was admired so much by us all," it said.

It ended by saying John's body would be released later that evening. This was done in an orderly fashion amid scenes of great grief but little trouble. And John was buried quietly by his friends.

Palace rocked as Salomé gives her story to the press
Salome's story is reflected in Mt 14:1–12 and Mk 6:14–29.

KILLING OF JOHN SHOCKS NATION

AT LAKE GALILEE, 31 AD

The country was still reeling this week following revelations of the circumstances surrounding the death of the preacher John at King Herod's palace last month. Neither Governor Pilate nor the religious authorities made any public comment on the matter.

Surprisingly, there were no scenes of public disorder involving John's friends and supporters. Most seemed stunned by the events and kept a low profile. Meanwhile a rumour spread that John's cousin Jesus might also have been killed, as he had not been seen for days.

He had been to visit his sick friend Lazarus in Bethany but didn't stay there too long. It was said he had been advised to go somewhere safer, when news of the circumstances surrounding John's death emerged.

Martha and Mary, Lazarus's sisters, said on Wednesday however they were very concerned about Jesus's whereabouts. He had left them two days before and, though he promised to send them a message before sunset, they had not heard from him. "This is not like him at all," said Mary, "and he was so worried about Lazarus."

To add fuel to their fears it was reported that King Herod has been taking a particular interest in Jesus. Palace sources confirmed the king had speculated that Jesus was John back from the dead.

The king had heard of the many miracles attributed to

Jesus. One source recalled him saying: "John, the man I beheaded, has been raised from the dead", when told about Jesus's healing powers, his walking on Lake Galilee, and his feeding of 5,000 people with a few loaves and fish. Another source at the palace attributed the comment simply to guilt on Herod's part. "He has been deeply agitated since John died. His doctors say he is sleeping very little and has terrible nightmares," the source said.

It was recalled that on the evening John was beheaded the king had become very distressed when Salomé asked for the preacher's head. One of the guests recalled: "It was clear he did not want to have John killed. He had admired John as a holy man. Herodias was to blame for it all. She saw his hesitation when Salomé asked for John's head and she kept repeating: 'You promised her anything ... anything.' Finally he gave in."

Some of the king's doctors are said to fear for his mental health, while it is said Herodias is becoming increasingly impatient with him and his "lily-livered weakness" as she is believed to have put it.

Salomé has left the country and is said to be staying abroad with friends.

Then it was reported that Jesus was seen on the shores of Lake Galilee. And, though his popularity had plummeted after his "I am the bread of life" address some weeks ago, people began to seek him out again. Some wanted to see whether he was really Jesus or John raised from the dead.

By the lake on Friday, asked by a man where he had been, Jesus said: "Foxes have holes and the birds have their nests but this son of Man has no place to lay his head." The man he spoke to, believed to be a teacher, said to him: "Sir, I will follow you anywhere, regardless."

Killing of John shocks nation
See Mt 4:3–12; Mk 6:14–29; Jn 11:1–6. See also Lk 9:57–62.

Woman of the Night Wrecks Party

CAPERNAUM, 31 AD

Further controversy has surrounded the preacher Jesus following a recent incident at the home of Simon, a local Pharisee.

An article in the *Moon* tabloid on Tuesday, titled "Jesus's Women", reported Simon explaining how he invited the preacher for dinner one evening recently. "I had heard so many of the stories. It seemed like the makings of a good night," he said.

Shortly after Jesus and the other guests arrived at Simon's house, a well-known local woman knocked on the door.

She demanded to see the preacher. Simon tried to get her to leave, She refused. Simon was deeply embarrassed, wondering what the guests might think. But she would not leave. "Eventually I had no choice. I had to let her in," he said.

She stood beside Jesus and began to weep. "It was awful. My wife was mortified," Simon recalled. Then the woman began to wet Jesus's feet with her tears and to kiss them. She wiped his feet with her hair and poured perfume on them.

"It was excruciating. My other guests didn't know where to look. He just lay there as if it was the most normal thing in the world. If he was a prophet, I thought to myself, he would know the sort of woman who was touching him like that." Simon was about to say this when Jesus said: "Simon,

I've a story for you."

"Two men owed money to a moneylender. One owed him 500 denarii and the other 50. Neither could pay him back. So, decent man that he was, he cancelled their debts. Now tell me which of the two loved him the most?" Simon answered: "Probably the man with the biggest debt." "You're right" said Jesus. "Do you see this woman? I came to your house. You gave me no water for my feet but she has washed them with her tears and wiped them dry with her hair. You didn't give me the customary kiss but since she came here she has not stopped kissing my feet.

"You did not put any oil in my hair but she has poured perfume on my feet. She may have done much that was wrong but it is all forgiven because she has loved much. And, Simon, remember whoever forgives little loves little." Jesus then turned to the woman and said: "All that you've done wrong is forgiven." Simon said some of his other guests were very annoyed at this, indeed at the entire incident. "Who is he to forgive sins?" was one angry comment Simon overheard. Jesus told the woman to go in peace. "Your faith has saved you," he told her, and she left happy.

"The night was ruined. It was all downhill then. Jesus left not long afterwards and my guests, well, speculated....," Simon told the tabloid.

Some of the guests said Jesus was surrounded by women all the time. "His friendship with the two sisters Martha and Mary came in for a lot of discussion," Simon told the *Moon*. "Then there is Mary from Magdala, now called Mary Magdalene I believe, who is well known to men in this part of the country. And there is Joanna, wife of Cuza, the manager of King Herod's household. My guests were amazed Cuza allowed her spend so much time with Jesus. But she is a strong-willed woman.

"And there is Suzanna ... and so, so many others. As well as their time, and who knows what else, these women are among the main financial supporters of the Jesus campaign," he said.

"Most of the men at my house that night were baffled by this. They could not understand what women saw in Jesus. But the women all agreed he was charismatic. 'A sort of innocence. The little-boy-lost look. You feel you can trust him and he is very attractive ... even if he is from Nazareth', was how one of my female guests explained it. Strange creatures!" commented Simon.

Woman of the night wrecks party
For differing perspectives on these events, and on the character of the woman involved, see Mt 26:6–13; Mk 14:3–9; Lk 7:36–50 and Jn 12:1–9.

Spin doctor's rift with preacher deepens

Jerusalem, 32 AD

It has been confirmed that the preacher Jesus has relegated his spokesman Mr Judas Iscariot to an advisory role following a row last week.

It has been clear recently that Mr Iscariot has been unhappy with some of the addresses given by Jesus—notably his "I am the bread of life" talk—which Mr Iscariot felt would alienate most devout Jews.

However, others among Jesus's supporters have been as critical of Mr Iscariot, believing he has a distinct preference for style over substance. One such source said: "It really does appear that all Judas is interested in is how things will look. The truth doesn't bother him at all. Succeeding is all that interests him."

Others close to Jesus have also been concerned about what they felt was Mr Iscariot's undue influence over the content of Jesus's policy. That too appears to have been checked.

Two addresses by Jesus last weekend appear to have been the catalyst for Mr Iscariot's relegation. Sources indicate he objected strenuously to both, saying they amounted to "political suicide" for the campaign. Jesus again objected to the use of the word "campaign" to describe what he was about, repeating once more that his business was "truth".

Preaching in Galilee, Jesus denounced most of the prominent towns in the province which he had visited recently. They had not responded to him but continued in their old ways. He cursed Korazin, Bethsaida and Capernaum in particular. If what they had seen and heard, had been seen and heard in Tyre and Sidon, "they would be in sackcloth and ashes," he said.

But he went further. "If the miracles that were performed in you were performed in Sodom it would be still with us," he said. Sodom was a notorious city which it was widely believed was destroyed by God for its wicked ways. On judgement day, Jesus said, God would be kinder to Sodom than to the Galilean towns named. In many eyes his comments were an invitation to vicious attack from the towns he had so mercilessly criticised.

He praised those few who supported him. He praised God because he had "hidden these truths from the wise and educated and revealed them to children". And, in an unexpected aside, he urged all who were tired and overwrought to come to him. "I will give you rest ... I am gentle and humble. You will find rest for your souls. For my yoke is easy and my burden light." Not for the first time his meaning was not at all clear. Which is one reason why he has so badly needed spin doctors.

But it would appear that it was an incident last Saturday that proved the final straw for his relationship with Mr Iscariot. Jesus and some friends were walking through a field of wheat. Some of them picked the heads off the wheat and ate them.

Some Pharisees saw this and, ever alert to pounce on Jesus, said to him: "Look. Your friends are breaking the

Sabbath." Even such things are forbidden by the law of God on a Saturday, according to the Pharisees.

Jesus reminded them that their great hero, King David, had done worse. "He and his friends went into the house of God and ate the consecrated bread." (Only priests are allowed to do so.) He asked whether they knew the law at all, then really set the cat among the pigeons by telling them "someone greater than the Temple is here", and that "the Son of Man is Lord of the Sabbath". Words which enraged the Pharisees and plunged Mr Iscariot into despair.

This was compounded later in a nearby synagogue. A man with a deformed hand asked Jesus to heal it. Again the Pharisees were ready for him. "Is it lawful to heal on the Sabbath?" they asked. And he was ready for them. "If one of your sheep fell into a drain on the Sabbath would you not get it out? And how much more important is a man than a sheep! So, take it from me, it is lawful to do good any day, even on the Sabbath." And he cured the man.

The Pharisees saw this as "blasphemous defiance" and talked darkly among themselves about what should be done with him. When they left, Mr Iscariot exploded at Jesus. He will not do so again.

Spin doctor's rift with preacher deepens
Mt 11:20–30; Mt 12:1–14; Mk 2:18–28; Mk 3:1–6; Lk 6:6–11.

Preacher Causes Some Surprise
in Farm Circles

Jerusalem, 32 AD

Some surprise has been expressed in the city at the knowledge Jesus the preacher has recently shown about tillage and horticulture matters.

"Considering his background it came out of the blue," said Job Muckanall, Agriculture Correspondent with the *Palestinian Times.* "I mean his father is a chippie in Nazareth. He was a chippie himself. And in Nazareth they wouldn't know a ploughed field if it stood up and bit them. As for mustard trees, the last tree of any sort they had up there went out with Methusaleh. It's a surprise alright.

"And his mother's people … weren't they shepherds from down south someplace? On either side they hadn't a field between them. Joseph was a great man for the session though," and he recalled a story about a wedding they were both at years ago. It was a good wedding.

Mr Muckanall's views have been reflected in comment by other experts in the field. Still more people were perplexed as to why Jesus should be talking about such matters at all. "Is he promoting a new tillage policy?" wondered Mr Muckanall. "That'd be a bit daft. There's nothing in tillage these days. Olives now, that's the way to go. The Roman's go crazy for them."

The comments followed reports from Lake Galilee where Jesus was talking from a boat to crowds about a farmer planting seed. "… and when he scattered the seed some fell along the path he walked on and the birds ate it. Some fell on rocky ground. It sprouted quickly, but when the hot summer sun came it withered and died because it had no roots. Other seed fell among thorns which choked it. And some fell on good soil. It produced a crop, a 100, 60 or 30 times what was sown."

No one understood him. "So …?" a man in the crowd said to a friend. Jesus continued: "The kingdom of heaven is like a man who sowed good wheat seed in his field. While everyone was asleep an enemy came and sowed weeds in with the wheat. When the wheat sprouted so did the weeds. The man's servants said to him, 'Will we pull up the weeds?' He said not to 'because when you pull the weeds you might pull up some of the wheat too. Let them grow together and when harvest time comes we will first collect the weeds and tie them in bundles for burning. Then we will gather the wheat'."

"So …?" said the man in the crowd to his friend, again. By which time Jesus was telling the crowd the kingdom of heaven was like a mustard seed. "The kingdom of heaven seems to be a lot of things today," said the man.

"Though it is among the smallest of seeds when it grows it is the largest of garden plants and becomes a tree. Even birds can perch in its branches," said Jesus. He continued: "The kingdom of heaven is like yeast that is mixed with a large amount of flour until it works through all the dough."

"Ah for God's sake. Come on. We're out of here. I've enough of this," said the man to his friend. They left, as did most of the crowd. By which time Jesus was in intense conversation with his friends.

"Jesus! Why, oh why, do you have to talk to the people in parables. Why in God's name can't you just tell it to them straight. Did one person out there understand what you were talking about?" they asked. "He who has ears to hear, let him hear," said Jesus. "The seed is the word of God. Some people are like the seed on the pathway. As soon as they hear it, it is snatched away by the devil. Those in a rocky place cannot hold onto it. Others, like the seed among thorns, are distracted by life's worries and temptations. And the seed on good soil? ... Well you can figure that out for yourselves. It's obvious," he said.

"As for the weeds ... the field is the world and the good seed is good men like you. The weeds are sons of the devil, planted by him. And just as the farmer pulls the weeds and has them burned so it will be at the end of time. These bad men will be thrown into the fiery furnace and there will be weeping and gnashing of teeth, but the good will shine like the sun. He who has ears, let him hear," he said.

"Now why didn't you say that in the first place?" asked one of his friends.

Preacher causes some surprise in farm circles
Mt 13:4–32; Mk 4:1–20; Lk 8:4–15.

REMARK MADE BY PREACHER
CAUSES UPROAR IN CAPITAL

JERUSALEM, 32 AD

The preacher Jesus, whose campaign is attracting increasing attention in the capital, has been quoted as saying there were some people he would like to see thrown over a cliff. The comment has caused uproar among the religious authorities once again, some of whom see it as incitement to kill.

A spokesman for the High Priest, Dr Caiaphas, said it was "just the latest example of this fellow getting away with next to murder. Surely it is about time the Governor intervened before someone is killed because of something this Jesus character says. For example the way he talks about the Pharisees alone must provide sufficient grounds for his arrest and long-term detention. It simply cannot go on like this. Someone will die …"

At Governor Pilate's palace the response was the now familiar, "… it is not Governor Pilate's practice to interfere in the internal affairs of this country unless that is absolutely necessary."

A spokesman for King Herod said it was unclear whether Jesus made the remark in his kingdom. Sources close to the king said he was anxious to detain Jesus who, since the "unfortunate" death of the preacher John, is regarded as troublemaker number one by the administration.

In fact, Jesus made the controversial remark in Capernaum. His friends had been arguing about which of them was the greatest. Not an unusual conversation. Jesus asked what they were arguing about, but they were too embarrassed to tell him. He knew anyhow.

He sat them down and said: "Whoever among you wants to be first must be the last and at the service of all." He called over a child and, taking the boy in his arms, said to the group: "You see this child. Unless you become like him you'll never see heaven. Whoever becomes as innocent as this child will be the greatest in heaven, and whoever welcomes a little child like this welcomes me."

Then he became very angry and continued: "But, I tell you, anyone who causes one of these little ones who believe in me to do wrong ... well ... it would be better for him to have a huge millstone hung around his neck and be thrown off a cliff into the depths of the sea."

Jesus's friends were surprised at the vehemence with which he spoke. But, though the preacher rarely became angry, they knew he had a temper. Some of them still spoke of his rage when he cleared the Temple in Jerusalem

Jesus, as enraged as then again, said: "There will be no pity for the one who causes people to do evil." And, in a comment that most of his friends thought over-the-top, he said: "If your hand or your foot causes you to do wrong, cut it off, throw it away. It is better for you to be maimed or crippled than to have two hands or two feet and end up in hell. If your eye makes you do wrong, gouge it out ... throw it away. It is better to have just one eye than have two and end up in hell."

Stroking the child's head he said: "Never look down on one of these little ones ... they are very precious to my father."

The preacher's own fondness for children was frequently commented on. It was not as well known, however, that Joseph, his father, also felt such affection.

Indeed, when it came to curing people with ailments Jesus never hesitated when a child was involved. He even, as some believe, raised the 12-year-old daughter of the rabbi Jairus from the dead.

People brought their children with them when he spoke, whether in a synagogue or in the open air. It often meant that with crying or playing children, people could not hear what he said. This led his friends to plead with people not to bring their children to these meetings.

Jesus heard about this. At the very next meeting people were bringing their children for him to touch as usual, when his friends rebuked them. Jesus became angry and said to them: "Let the children come to me and don't try to stop them again. Heaven belongs to such as these … anyone who doesn't accept God and heaven with the innocence of a child will never see eternal life."

He took the children in his arms and embraced them. And his friends were suitably chastened.

Remark made by preacher causes uproar in capital
For Jesus's discourse, see Mt 18: 1-11; Mk 9:33-44; Lk 9:46 50 and also Lk 17:1-2. For his special love for children see Mt 19:13-15; Mk 10:13-16; Lk 18:15-17. Compare also Mt 9:18-26; Lk 8:40-56

DEATH OF LAZARUS
COMES AS A GREAT SHOCK

JERUSALEM, 32 AD

The death took place in Bethany, last week, of Lazarus, a member of the prominent local wine-producing family. A native of the village, which is about three kilometers from Jerusalem, he was just 32.

He had been ill for some time but his death, while not unexpected, still came as a great shock to family and friends. He had not been married and is survived by two sisters, Martha and Mary.

His funeral on Saturday was one of the largest ever seen in Judaea. It was accompanied by heart-rending grief, particularly when the stone was rolled across the entrance to his tomb, sealing off his remains for eternity. Both sisters remain inconsolable. As well as being a highly successful businessman, until his recent illness, Lazarus was the proverbial "life and soul" wherever two or three were gathered. His appetite for life and company was insatiable, as was his generosity to friends and even the anonymous needy. It was said he made many donations he could not remember subsequently.

He was also a gifted storyteller with a wonderful talent for mimicry. Among his many favourite tales was the recent one of a wedding he attended at Cana with his close friend, the preacher Jesus. The wine ran out early in the celebrations and his account of the ensuing panic was hilarious. Jesus did not attend the funeral. Nor has he been in contact with

Martha or Mary. They are said to be deeply hurt by his inexplicable insensitivity.

In Jerusalem, it has been speculated since that Jesus is fearful of arrest and is avoiding all places he would be expected to be. He visited Lazarus, Martha and Mary, in Bethany shortly before Lazarus became ill, but did not stay long. Indeed, on that occasion he criticised Martha for fussing.

When he arrived Mary sat down and they chatted for hours while Martha worked around the house. Eventually, Martha got fed up with this and said to Jesus, "Doesn't it matter to you that she has left all the work for me to do while she sits there nattering with you? Tell her to help me!"

But Jesus replied, "Martha, Martha, take it easy. You worry too much about too many things. Just take one thing at a time. Mary is the one who is right." Martha was furious.

She is said to have told friends afterwards that Jesus had lost the run of himself. "He is not a bit like he used to be. You know, I think he actually believes those things he says about himself," is what one friend said she remarked at the time. But it had not been possible to confirm this. It was recalled in Jerusalem over the weekend that Jesus had once told a young man to "let the dead bury the dead". The young man had said he would follow Jesus as soon as he buried his father.

Remembering this, a source at the High Priests' Office said Jesus's absence from Lazarus's funeral was "just the latest example of the coldhearted lack of human compassion this fellow is capable of. What he does not seem to realise, or care about, is that funerals are for the living and not the dead. Are we to conclude that poor Martha and Mary are now among the dead who must bury the dead?" he asked.

It is also rumoured that Jesus had known of Lazarus's death since the evening it happened, but still refused to go to Bethany. True or otherwise, this story has encouraged even deeper hostility towards him. A friend of the preacher, who said he was with Jesus when he was told the news, was quoted as saying his response was not one of grief but "almost of joy".

He said something on the lines of, "This has happened to bring glory to God and through it to his son, who will also receive glory". The friend, who did not wish to be named, said, "I don't know what he meant, but sure we don't know half the things he means, half the time."

Death of Lazarus comes as a great shock
For the death of Lazarus see Jn 11:1–16. For Jesus's visit with Mary and Martha look at Lk 10:38–42.

RISE OF LAZARUS SEEN AS ELABORATE TRICK

BETHANY, 32 AD

This village, about three kilometres from Jerusalem, has been thronged with sightseers all week following some of the most extraordinary events ever witnessed in Judaea.

Lazarus, who was buried here last Saturday week, has been giving interviews to hordes of media people and the just plain curious since he emerged from his tomb on Tuesday last. Everywhere he has been mobbed by those who believe he rose from the dead and by the sceptical, who shout insults at him. For his part he has said repeatedly he remembers "nothing" since losing consciousness two weeks ago.

"It's as though I've had a long deep sleep," he said, "I feel great." But he still believed in life after death, he said.

This latest saga began with the arrival of the preacher Jesus in Bethany on Tuesday. A close friend of Lazarus's, he missed the funeral, which in itself caused considerable and frequently uncharitable speculation. Many friends of Lazarus were still in the village comforting the dead man's two sisters, Martha and Mary, when he arrived.

Martha went to meet him but Mary stayed at home. "If you had been here my brother would not have died," Martha said to him, more in sorrow than in anger, though it made little sense to those listening to her. "Your brother will rise again," Jesus said. "Yeah sure ... on the last day!" Martha responded.

Then Jesus launched into another of his strange speeches. "I am the resurrection and the life. Whoever believes in me will live, even if he dies, and whoever lives and believes in me will never die. Do you believe this?" he asked Martha. She said she did, though like most people there she didn't seem to have a clue what he was talking about.

Mary then arrived at the scene. The crowd expected fireworks, as Mary was known to have a temper and was said to be very angry at Jesus for missing the funeral.

In what some interpreted as an accusatory tone she said to Jesus: "If you had been here he wouldn't have died." Just as Martha had done. People began to wonder whether Jesus had some rare cure for Lazarus's illness. Jesus said nothing.

He saw how Mary wept and seemed unable to speak. "Where is he buried?" he asked eventually. They brought him to the tomb and he ... sank. The grief closed in about his head and he wept. And he wept. People in the crowd began to weep too. "He really did love him," some said. Others were less generous. "If, as they say, he can make the blind see he could have saved Lazarus from dying," they said.

"Take away the stone," Jesus commanded, referring to the stone blocking the entrance to the tomb. "But Jesus," began an alarmed Martha, "there'll be a bad smell. He's in there four days." And the weather had been very hot.

Jesus insisted. The stone was moved and he called out, "Lazarus my friend, come on out." And to the horror of the crowd, some of whom ran away, Lazarus came out, his grave clothes hanging off him. Jesus embraced his old friend with tears in his eyes. Martha and Mary were beside themselves with shock, wonder, and joy.

"No Sex After Death?" proclaimed the *Moon* tabloid in

a front page headline the next day. It had another story on Lazarus headlined "HOAX". The *Palestinian Times* headlined its story of the event: "Lazarus: Probably In Deep Coma." It quoted a medical report on a rare illness that has all the symptoms of death. "'Nothing' After Death" read a headline in the *Judaea Humanist.*

A spokesman for the High Priest, Dr Caiaphas, dismissed the Lazarus story as "an elaborate trick". He said it was designed to shore up slipping support for the Jesus campaign and was in fact an indication of the desperation to which that campaign had now descended. When it was put to him that people who were at the scene believed Lazarus had been dead and rose again he commented: "Some people are prepared to believe anything. After all, remember there are those who believe the Earth is round when the evidence of their own eyes tells them it is flat. There are fools everywhere. Even in Judaea."

Rise of Lazarus seen as elaborate trick
Compare Jn 11:17–45.

CAIAPHAS SUES OVER REPORT
ON A PLOT TO KILL JESUS

JERUSALEM, 32 AD

The High Priest, Dr Caiaphas, has begun libel proceedings against the *Palestinian Times* newspaper following a report on Tuesday which said he was party to a plot to kill the preacher Jesus.

Iscariot and Iscariot (Jerusalem) Solicitors had sent a letter to the newspaper in advance of the report. It said it was aware the report was planned and warned that, if published, it would constitute "a grave defamation of our client".

It said proceedings of the Sanhedrin, the inner council of chief priests where the newspaper said the plot was discussed by Dr Caiaphas, were "of necessity in confidence", and that, "any report which you may publish about such proceedings will constitute a grave violation of this principle."

Its client would not hesitate in instigating all such proceedings as may be necessary to remedy any consequence of publication, it said. The newspaper published the report anyhow.

It said that following the reappearance of Lazarus at Bethany last week a meeting of the Sanhedrin was called to discuss "the Jesus problem". Claims that he had performed miracles; that he was the Messiah; and now that he raised the dead "had simply got out of hand", one of the chief priests said.

"If we let him go on like this everyone will believe in him and then the Romans will turn on the whole lot of us.

They will see him as a threat to their rule," he said. Dr Caiaphas is then alleged to have said: "It is better for one man to die than for us all to be killed." The newspaper reported the meeting then discussed various plans to have Jesus killed.

As well as initiating legal proceedings, Dr Caiaphas issued a strongly worded statement describing the *Times* report as "outrageous". "That a responsible newspaper should stoop so low is a further and worrying indication of the depths to which the media have sunk," he said.

He compared the report to one in the same newspaper some months ago which said the preacher John had been beheaded by King Herod as a gift to his step-daughter Salomé after she danced for his dinner guests. The palace said John had been killed accidentally when he was mistaken by a (since deceased) executioner for another prisoner.

"And I notice the august *Times* has yet to apologise for that shocking report," Dr Caiaphas added.

Since the "plot" report was published Jesus has stopped appearing in public. He spent some of last week in Ephraim (formerly known as Oprah), a village on the edge of the desert. He also spent time with Lazarus in Bethany. A dinner was given in his honour in the village on Thursday night. It was prepared by Lazarus's sister, Martha.

To the discomfort of some guests, including friends of Jesus, Lazarus's other sister Mary poured a pint of nard perfume on his feet and then wiped them with her hair. Nard is probably the most expensive perfume on the market.

Judas, treasurer to the Jesus campaign and its sometime publicity director, was unhappy about this. Recently there have been unsubstantiated rumours about his handling of campaign funds.

"Why wasn't this perfume sold instead and the money given to the poor. It must have been worth at least a year's wages," he said. Jesus was dismissive. "Leave her alone," he said, "she was meant to save this for the day of my burial."

This comment was greeted with laughter as guests saw it as Jesus being ironic following the reports of a plot to kill him. "You will always have the poor but you won't always have me," he continued and they laughed again, believing he was still being funny.

Judas, however, was angered still further by the comments. He interpreted them literally and commented to another guest about Jesus's "growing arrogance". He said: "He really thinks he's going to save the world, you know."

The guest then suddenly thumped the table. "Now I have it ...," he said and laughed. He had just understood graffiti he had seen on a wall in Jerusalem which read: "Jesus Saves, Judas Invests."

Caiaphas sues over report on a plot to kill Jesus
Regarding a plot against Jesus or Lazarus, see Mt 26:1–5;
Lk 20: 19–26; Jn 11:45–57. As for the anointing of Jesus at Bethany,
look at Jn 12:1-9 and compare Mt 26:6–13.

LAZARUS WISHES
HE WAS BACK IN THE TOMB

JERUSALEM, 32 AD

A report that the council of chief priests, the Sanhedrin, was plotting to kill the preacher Jesus was resurrected this week following an allegation that they also planned to kill his friend Lazarus.

Both stories have been vigorously denied by the religious authorities as "scandalous, outrageous, scurrilous." Or "SOS", as it was headlined in the *Moon* tabloid.

Some weeks ago it was claimed Jesus had raised Lazarus from the dead. This was dismissed as "an elaborate trick" by the Sanhedrin. But since then vast crowds have been descending on Bethany, the village where Lazarus lives. They go there to see the once dead man. Many of them are saying Jesus is the Messiah.

A report in the *Palestinian Times* this week said reliable sources had indicated members of the Sanhedrin believed the situation in Bethany was "out of control". Plans to kill Lazarus were "under active discussion". Jesus, meanwhile, has not been seen all week.

Predictably perhaps, the letters columns of the *Palestinian Times* have been filled with speculation as to whether in law it is possible to die twice. The legitimacy of Lazarus's current existence has been extensively explored, as has his status as a man of property.

Legal experts have responded that, were the claims about Lazarus true, the situation would be unprecedented and "make an ass of the law". A reader replied that, as it was not possible for something to change into what it already was, "then surely the law would become something different. A bird brain perhaps?"

The legal experts concluded however that, as it was believed the Lazarus episode was indeed an "elaborate trick" to boost the Jesus campaign, all such speculation was "mere entertainment".

For his part Lazarus is said to be finding current pressures difficult. He has retreated to his home and is not giving interviews. Last Tuesday his clothes were nearly torn off as crowds rushed to touch him. A man at the scene said it was "disgraceful. He probably wishes he was back in the tomb. At least there he had peace and quiet."

It also emerged this week that some time ago Jesus had forecast he would be killed in Jerusalem by the authorities, including the chief priests. He also said he would rise again, three days afterwards.

Sources close to the campaign recalled that when Jesus announced this, Peter, one of his closest supporters, reacted: "Never, my friend. That will not happen as long as there's breath in my body." Jesus turned and told him he was the devil himself. This shocked everyone.

Jesus has become more volatile lately. "You are a stumbling block ...," he told Peter. "You're only thinking of this world, not of God."

Peter was devastated. Just a few days earlier Jesus had told him he was the rock on which he would build his new administration. Not even hell itself would be able to touch it, he said. He went further and said that whatever laws Peter made would apply in heaven as well as on earth.

Even some of his friends thought that was a bit much, like his claim about rising from the dead in three days. But they let both pass as typical examples of Jesus's fondness for hyperbole.

That "rock" incident happened at Caesarea Philippi after Jesus asked them who they believed he really was. Peter piped up that he was "the Christ, the son of the living God", which some of the friends thought a very clever move. It was clear to them that Peter and John were vying to be Jesus's deputy in the new administration. But even they felt it was over-the-top to say Jesus was "the Christ".

Jesus, it was obvious, bought into the idea too. He told Peter he was "blessed" to know what he did and that his knowledge came not from men but from his father in heaven. This also caused confusion.

"Jesus's father is in Nazareth, and that is as far from heaven as you'll get, and Simon Peter's father is still in Capernaum. What's going on here?" was how another of Jesus's friends reacted. He did not wish to be named.

He continued that "Jesus then, in all seriousness, told us not to tell anyone he was the Christ. Even he must realise how ludicrous it is. He'd be the laughing stock of Palestine if that got out."

Lazarus wishes he was back in the tomb
See Jn 12:9–11 and also Mt 26:1–5. As to predictions of Jesus's passion, compare Mt 16:31–33, 17:22–23, 20:17–19 with Lk 9:22, 9:44–45, 18:31–34.

BAD END TO PREACHER FORECAST

JERUSALEM, 32 AD

At an extraordinary, indeed unprecedented, press conference in the city last Saturday the High Priest, Dr Caiaphas, denounced reports that he and the council of chief priests, the Sanhedrin, were plotting to kill the preacher Jesus and his friend Lazarus.

"Despite repeated denials from me and other priests, people still insist on believing these shocking lies," he said. "I would remind them that the eighth commandment, handed down by God himself, says you must not lie. That also covers taking away people's good name by rumour."

Pointing directly at a reporter from the *Palestinian Times* newspaper, which has carried such reports over the past two weeks, he said: "I do not have plans for that man." He reminded those present that he and his colleagues on the Sanhedrin were men of God.

"Our job is to uphold his laws, another of which is 'you must not kill'—the fifth commandment. Do you think we are such hypocrites as to uphold that law on the one hand while planning to break it on the other?" The question was not answered.

Dr Caiaphas admitted the Sanhedrin was "very unhappy" about the Jesus campaign. He agreed it had been discussed at successive meetings. "You must understand he is making a laughing-stock of our religion, and not just here but before the eyes of the world. We all know what the Romans think of us already. We really do not need to have a fellow Jew hold all of us up to ridicule in such a provocative fashion."

He also accused Jesus of "the most blatant blasphemy". "He has claimed to be the Messiah, the son of God. It's outrageous. Blasphemy is a capital offence, you know." He rejected suggestions that he and the Sanhedrin might be seeking Jesus's death on a charge of blasphemy. "We don't want to see anyone die," he said. "That is not our way at all."

He was "deeply concerned" however at the many people who believed Jesus's claims about himself. "Poor, ignorant people, with no education. Simple fishermen from the shores of Lake Galilee. What do they know about anything? And he has persuaded them to leave their wives and children to follow him. What sort of 'Son of God' would do that sort of irresponsible thing?" he asked.

He was dismissive of the miracles attributed to Jesus. "Faithhealing probably" was how he explained them. "People convinced they would be cured and then getting well. It's not rare, you know." Reports of Jesus walking on water, calming winds, changing water to wine, raising the dead, he said, were "stories, stories, stories, probably dreamed up by his fishermen when they were drunk. You know the reputation they have in Capernaum for drink."

Speaking about Jesus, he said: "I regret to put it like this, but the man's a charlatan. He has even convinced those fishermen that he was born in Bethlehem. In a stable! And that he is of the line of David, as foretold by the prophets. The truth is he was born in Nazareth, that his father is the carpenter Joseph, and that his mother is Joseph's second wife Mary.

"In fact, according to our research, he is illegitimate. Mary was betrothed to Joseph when he discovered she was pregnant. She told him a story about some fellow called Gabriel, who she said was 'an angel'." He laughed at this point. "And, though pregnant, she insisted that she had still not lost her virginity. How about that?" He laughed again. Everyone else laughed too.

"Joseph, decent man that he was, married her anyway. What would have become of her otherwise? Besides he needed a mother for the rest of his children."

Caiaphas continued that Jesus was "just an idle layabout with no interest in anything but causing trouble. He likes too much wine and to surround himself with women. What sort of Messiah is that? My own view is that he wants to be a second John, the preacher who died so tragically some time back. "But Jesus is little more than a cheap imitation. He wouldn't be worthy to tie John's sandal straps. He wasn't even a good carpenter, and he has poor Joseph's heart broken. He'll come to a bad end all right, but it will have nothing to do with me or the Sanhedrin, I can assure you of that," he said.

Bad end to preacher forecast
Look at Mt 26:1–5; Lk 20:19–26 and Jn 11:47–53, 12:10–11. With regard to the origins of Jesus see Mt 2:1–25 and Lk 1:26–38. But compare also Mt 1:1–18; Lk 3:23–38 and Jn 1:1–14.

VIEWS OF PREACHER
UPSET POWERS THAT BE

JERUSALEM, 33 AD

The preacher Jesus was at the centre of further controversy this week following publication of the bi-monthly *Cool Press* magazine on Thursday. He featured as guest in its Mad Chatter Box spot, a generally light-hearted series of off-beat questions and answers, usually involving well-known people. Jesus' replies annoyed the authorities, both civil and religious. A spokesman for the High Priest Dr Caiaphas said "this frothy nonsense is a true indication of the mind of this so-called preacher. He's a joke." A spokesman for King Herod said the replies were "not worthy of response" while Governor Pilate's office said "it's just a bit of fun after all." Below we publish the Jesus Mad Chatter column in full.

1. **Who would be the last person you would invite to your birthday party?** Dr Caiaphas (he might make it my last).

2. **Who would be the first person you would invite to your birthday party?** Lazarus. He's good fun. He could organise it, too. And he owes me.

3. **Favourite saying?** "… for the love of God."

4. **Favourite book?** Genesis. It makes me feel nostalgic.

5. **Favourite author?** King David. I just love those psalms. "The Lord is my shepherd, I shall not want,/He makes me lie down in green pastures,/he leads me beside quiet waters,/he restores my soul…" Beautiful…

6. **Favourite actor/actress?** Judas Iscariot. There's a bit of 'oul

Nick about him. He's truly gifted and has yet to be found out by the others.

7. **Most embarrassing moment?** At that wedding in Cana. When my mother asked me to organise more wine ... in front of everyone ... I had never done anything like that before. Luckily it worked out alright.

8. **Favourite food/drink?** A good wine. You can't beat it.

9. **Most desirable date?** Easter Sunday.

10. **Favourite method of relaxation?** Having women pour perfume over my feet and then dry them with their hair. Out of this world...

11. **If you weren't pursuing your present career, what other might you have chosen?** Running a vineyard probably.

12. **Biggest thrill?** I was twelve. With the priests in the Temple. I had them thoroughly confused.

13. **Biggest disappointment?** Judas.

14. **Your concept of heaven?** Many mansions.

15. **Your concept of hell?** Must be seen to be believed.

16. **Greatest ambition?** To make it through to Easter Sunday without caving in.

17. **Period of history you'd most like to have lived in, and why?** In the early days of the Garden of Eden. Everything was so much easier then. It's tougher than that now.

18. **If you weren't a human being, which animal would you have chosen to be?** A lamb probably.

19. **If you were told that the world was ending tomorrow morning how would you react, what would you do?** I'd be very surprised. Then I'd have a word with my father.

20. **Your nominee for the world's best dressed person.**

Solomon, in all his glory.

21. **Favourite term of abuse?** Get behind me, Satan?

22. **Biggest fear?** Crucifixion. Dying slowly on a cross, could anything be worse? It sends shivers down my spine.

23. **Humanity's most useful invention?** Wine.

24. **Humanity's most useless invention?** High Priests, kings … authorities generally.

25. **What would be your dying words?** "It's over."

It has not been possible to contact Jesus for clarification as to what he meant by "Easter" Sunday or his comments on his friend Judas Iscariot.

It has been known for some time that there have been serious strains between the two, but commentators now say a split is inevitable. Speculation has centred on whether any others of Jesus's core group of twelve will leave also.

It has been clear for some time that John is disillusioned at not being made Jesus's deputy, a position now held by Peter. But it is thought unlikely John would leave.

Views of preacher upset powers that be
For these events look at: Jn 11:1-44; Psalm 22(23); Jn 2: 1-11; Jn 12: 1-10; Isaiah 5: 1-7; Lk 2: 41-52; Mt 26: 36-46; Jn 19-20; Gen 2: 1-3:24; Jn 1: 29; Mt 6: 9-13; Lk 18: 31-34; Jn 8: 12-30.

JESUS RUFFLES FEATHERS OF PROUD

JERUSALEM, 33 AD

Vineyards were on Jesus's mind again this week and not without controversy. He was speaking to a crowd in Judaea when he compared heaven to a vineyard owner who went out in the morning to hire labourers.

The owner agreed a price for the day and the men began to work. A few hours later he hired more men. He did this again three hours, six hours, and eight hours later. As it was harvest time the working days were long.

When it came to pay time, the owner said to his foreman: "Call the men in and pay them their wages, beginning with the last ones hired and continuing backwards to those who have been here all day." And it transpired the men in last were paid the same as those who had worked all day.

The latter were angry at this. "These fellas who were hired last worked only an hour," they said, "and you paid them the same as us after all the work we have done all day?" He said to them: "Didn't you agree this morning to work for what I have just given you? If I want to pay these other men the same, that is a matter for me. It's my money. Are you envious because I am being generous?" Jesus did not say how the complaining workers responded. He finished the story by commenting, "the last will be first and first will be last." Which left his hearers puzzled—and not for the first time.

A spokesman for the Palestine Unskilled Persons

Society (PUPS) commented afterwards that Jesus's story was "disgraceful" and encouraged the abuse of workers by unscrupulous employers. "How can he possibly promote a policy which discriminates in favour of the rich?" he asked of Jesus, "especially when his own father is a working man and most of his followers too."

He suggested it was no wonder Jesus complained about the harvest being great and the labourers few. "Who'd want to work for someone like that," he remarked.

"Is he saying a man or woman shoouldn't get a fair day's wages for a fair day's work. He is discriminating against the working man and woman in favour of the layabout. And that's another thing. Where's the women in his story. Not one. Is he sexist as well as everything else?" he asked.

He also attacked Jesus for "actively promoting the wealthy and those in pursuit of wealth". The spokesman was referring to another of Jesus's stories. It concerned an owner ("See," said the spokesman, "the rich guy is always the good guy.") who entrusted his property to his staff as he was going on a journey.

As an incentive he gave one man five talents, another two talents and another one talent, to use "each according to his ability". The PUPS spokesman particularly liked that last line.

The owner went away. The man with the five talents put his money to work and made five more. The man with two talents made two more. But the man with one talent hid it in the ground.

Time passed and the owner returned. "Well done, good

and faithful servant," he said to the man who had made five talents, "I will put you in charge of many things." He said the same to the man who had made two talents.

But the man who had buried his talent said to the owner "I know you are a hard man, harvesting where you have not sown and gathering where you have not scattered seed. So I went out and hid your talent. Here it is!" And the owner was very angry. "You useless lazy good-for-nothing. Why didn't you even deposit it in a bank so I would have made interest?"

And he shouted to other staff that they were to take the talent and give it to the man who made the five talents. "For everyone who will have will be given more, and he will have abundance. Whoever does not have, even that will be taken from him. And throw that useless good-for-nothing out of here. Into the dark with him where there is only misery, with weeping and gnashing of teeth," he said.

The PUPS spokesman was furious. "If that is not a charter for greed and exploitation and active discrimination against the worker, I don't know what it is? And, of course, no women again. The sooner something is done about this Jesus fella the better."

Jesus ruffles feathers of proud
In conncection with these events, see Mt 20:1–16.

JESUS ALIENATES ZEALOTS, PRIESTS

JERUSALEM, 33 AD

The preacher Jesus has done the seemingly impossible in uniting Zealots and chief priests against him. Independent commentators said this week he seemed to have a death wish for his campaign.

Some have suggested he may have a death wish himself. This followed the preacher's assertion once again that he would be killed. "Melodrama, to raise flagging support," was the comment of an editorial in the *Palestinian Times*.

Most controversially, however, he told a story this week about a kind Samaritan man which enraged leaders of the Zealot paramilitaries as well as the religious authorities, though for different reasons.

It followed a report that Jesus had been asked by a theologian what he (the theologian) must do to gain eternal life. Jesus asked him what was written in the law of the prophets about this and the theologian quoted: "Love the Lord your God with all your heart and with all your soul and with all your strength and with all your mind," and, "Love your neighbour as yourself."

"Do that and you'll be all right," Jesus told him. But the theologian, who later admitted he really wanted to prove Jesus was out of line with the law of the prophets and so not really a good Jew, asked: "Who is my neighbour?"

Typically, Jesus didn't give a straight answer. He told a story about a man travelling on the road from Jerusalem to Jericho when, to no sensible person's surprise, he was attacked by thieves. They stripped the man, beat him up and left him for dead.

A priest passed and, though he saw the badly-beaten man, crossed to the other side of the road and continued on his journey. Then a Levite, who assist priests, came on the scene and he too passed by. Next came a Samaritan. He saw the man and was moved to tears. He bandaged his wounds and poured soothing oil on them, and wine to kill infection. Then he put the man on his donkey and took him to the nearest hotel and looked after him there.

The next day, before he set off on the rest of his journey, he gave money to the hotel manager and asked him to look after the wounded man until he returned. Any extra expense incurred would be paid when he came back, he said.

His story finished, Jesus turned to the theologian and asked: "Which of those three do you think was a neighbour to the man who fell among thieves?" And the theologian had to say, "the man who had mercy on him". Jesus told him: "Now you go and do the same."

A source at the Chief Priest's palace described the story as "typical. He cannot leave us alone. Every chance he gets he attacks the priests. It is a story after all, so why did the two who passed by have to be a priest and a Levite? They could have been fishermen. Or carpenters? His agenda becomes clearer daily."

A Zealot source said it was just a further example of Jesus's "love affair with the Samaritans. The way he goes on you'd think he was one of them himself. I mean the man in the story didn't have to be a Samaritan did he? And another thing, he told us we should pay our taxes to Caesar. He's not a real Galilean at all."

However, it appears the story Jesus told may have been true. In a letter to the *Palestinian Times*, a man claiming he was the priest who passed by, objected strenuously to the spin Jesus had put on it. He said that, on that particular day, earlier this year, he was already late for a talk in Jerusalem on "Sin and the Sabbath".

Besides, he believed the man was not badly injured, and he also thought that if he intervened the robbers would return and do the same to him. When he got to Jerusalem he reported the incident to the authorities in the belief they would take care of it.

When tracked down eventually by a reporter with the *Palestinian Times*, the Levite at first denied all knowledge of the incident. He has since changed jobs due to "a personal disagreement with God", as he put it. He now makes saddlebags. Finally admitting he had passed by the badly-injured man, he said: "What could I do? It happens all the time. I can't help everyone. Anyway, I didn't create the world. I only live here."

Jesus alienates Zealots, priests
For the question put to Jesus regarding the greatest
commandment, see Lk 10:25–28. Compare Mt 19:16–30
(as well as Mt 22:34–40 and Mt 16:1), Mk 10:17–21 and also
Lk 18:18-30. The parable of the Good Samaritan is told only
by Luke, Lk 10:29–37.

HOSTILE PREACHER
ROUNDS ON CHIEF PRIESTS

JUDAEA, 33 AD

An increasingly belligerent Jesus this week called the Pharisees and chief priests "hypocrites", "snakes", and "a brood of vipers". In his most provocative address to date, he told a crowd: "Do not do as they do. They don't practise what they preach. They tie up heavy loads and put them on people's backs and then won't lift a finger to help the poor devils they burden like that.

"Everything they do is for show. They love their fancy clothes and to sit at the top places in the synagogue or at functions. They love their status and to be greeted in the street with respect and to have people call them 'rabbi'.

"Don't call them 'rabbi'. You have only one master. Apart from him you are all equal. And don't call anyone on earth 'father'. You have only one spiritual father and he is in Heaven. The greatest among you will be your servant. Whoever exalts himself will be humbled and whoever humbles himself will be exalted.

"Woe to you teachers of the law and Pharisees. You hypocrites! You are like whitewashed tombs. Beautiful to look at but full of rottenness inside. You snakes! You brood of vipers!" He continued like that for 45 minutes.

When it was put to him that he was being unnecessarily provocative and that what he said was likely to cause great anger and offence, he said: "Do you think I have come to bring peace? I am telling you now I have come to bring division ... father against son and son against father, mother against daughter and daughter against mother ..."

Annoyed at the tendency of the Pharisees to stick rigidly to the letter of the law, whatever the circumstances, he said to the crowd: "When you see a cloud in the west, immediately you say 'it's going to rain'—and it does. And when the wind blows from the south, you say 'it's going to be hot'—and it is. You know how to read the sky. How is it you cannot read the times? Why don't you judge for yourselves what is right?" he asked them. And they were silent.

Last Saturday he had a vigorous encounter with a group of Pharisees not far from Jerusalem. He was speaking in a synagogue when he saw a woman bent double. She had been crippled for 18 years. He put his hands on her and immediately her back straightened.

The man in charge of the synagogue was furious. "There are six days for work. She could have been healed on any of those six days and not today, the Sabbath." Jesus was enraged. "Don't you untie your donkey on the Sabbath and bring him to water for a drink? Then why shouldn't this woman, a human being like you, be healed on the Sabbath?" This was met with sullen silence.

Later in the day he healed a man suffering from dropsy. This incident took place at the home of a Pharisee who was friendly towards Jesus. He had warned the preacher to leave the area as King Herod wanted to kill him.

Jesus responded: "Tell that old fox I will continue to heal people today, tomorrow, and the day after, and for as long as needs be, whatever he thinks."

But other Pharisees at the house were offended that Jesus should heal people on the Sabbath. "Is it right to heal on the Sabbath or isn't it?" they asked him, knowing the correct answer.

Jesus replied: "If one of you had a son or a beast fall into a drain on the Sabbath, would you leave it there until the following day? Wouldn't you pull him out immediately?" And they were silent again.

He noticed them rush to the top places at the dinner table. He said: "Don't do that. Don't take the top place when invited to dinner. You might be asked to give it up, for someone else. Then you'll be humiliated. Take the lowest place. More than likely your host will say, 'Hey, don't sit down there. Come on up,' and you'll be moved to a better place."

Later that evening it is said he stood on a hill overlooking Jerusalem in the distance below. He said: "Jerusalem, O Jerusalem. You kill the good and those sent to help you. How many times I would have loved to gather your people together in a warm embrace, as a hen gathers her chicks under her wings. But you will not see me again until you say 'Blessed is he who comes in the name of the Lord'." And no one knew what he was talking about.

Hostile preacher rounds on chief priests
For Jesus's remarks about the Pharisees and chief priests,
look at Mt 23:1–39 and compare Mk 12:38–39 and Lk 11:43.
Compare also the words of John the Baptist in Mt 3:7-10. For Jesus's remarks
about Jerusalem, see Mt 24:1-25.

JUDAEA'S YOUNG HAVE A LOT TO LEARN

JERUSALEM, 33 AD

A major overhaul of the system of religious education in Judaea has begun following a damning report published this week. Commissioned by the Sanhedrin, the council of chief priests, it concluded that the standard of religious knowledge among Jewish children was "truly abysmal" and "indeed, quite shocking".

It recommended "immediate and radical action to correct this totally unacceptable situation." The report, which was conducted throughout the country over the past six months among children under 10 years old, gave extensive examples of the ignorance of the children where knowledge of Jewish belief was concerned.

Without attribution, it quoted the authentic responses of some of the children as examples of a wider ignorance.

Describing the beginning of the world, an eight-year old boy in Jerusalem wrote that, "God got tired of creating the world, so he took the Sabbath off."

A seven-year-old girl, also in Jerusalem, wrote that, "Adam and Eve were created from an apple tree," and "Noah built an ark which the animals come onto in pears."

She continued that: "Lot's wife was a pillar of salt by day, but a ball of fire by night," and that, "Samson was a strongman who let himself be led astray by a Jezebel called Delilah."

A boy in Bethany wrote that, "Moses led the Hebrews to the Red Sea, where they made unleavened bread which is bread without any ingredients." He continued that, "the Egyptians were all drowned in the desert. Afterwards, Moses went up on Mount Cyanide to get the 10 amendments."

He continued that, "the first commandment was when Eve told Adam to eat the apple."

A young girl in Jericho wrote that, "the greatest miracle was when Joshua told his son to stand still and he obeyed him." In her opinion, "David was a Hebrew king skilled at playing the liar." She further claimed that, "Solomon, one of David's sons, had 300 wives and 700 porcupines."

A seven-year-old girl in a Bethlehem school wrote that, "a Jew should have only one spouse. This is called monotony." She also wrote about, "holy acrimony, which is another name for marriage."

An editorial in the *Palestinian Times* described the findings as "extremely serious" and "a sad reflection of the state of religious knowledge at a wider level in this society. It felt that "ultimately this is the parents' responsibility, but the religious authorities also have a case to answer."

It continued that, "regardless, the present situation cannot be allowed continue. It also goes some considerable way towards explaining why this country is beset by all sorts of preachers and so-called miracle workers, some even claiming to be the Messiah. A better-informed population, adults as well as children, would not be as easily taken-in by such fanatics if they were better informed about their religion."

The High Priest, Dr Caiaphas, agreed the situation was "unacceptable", but felt the media were "largely responsible for it. For years all they have done is attack, demean, denigrate, and generally dismiss anything to do with religion. And they are continually holding the religious authorities up to ridicule. This inevitably has had consequences, not least in the home. For some time it has been clear that people have less and less interest in religion. Children pick this up. So they have little incentive to learn."

He did, however, agree with the newspaper's suggestion that present levels of ignorance among the people made the country a rich breeding ground for religious fanatics. "Take this Jesus fellow for example. We are asked to believe this carpenter from Nazareth is the Messiah, the son of God. That he cures the sick and demented, walks on water, stops storms, changes water into wine, feeds thousands with a few loaves and fish, that he is transfigured on a mountain where God can be heard actually speaking to him, again!—and ... wait for it ... that he raises the dead! I ask you. The truly sad thing is that poor ignorant people believe in this guy. That is what all the bashing by the media has brought about. It has to stop. And he has to be stopped also."

Judaea's young have a lot to learn
The eight-year old Jerusalem boy was thinking of the story of Creation in The Book of Genesis, 1:1-2:3. The seven-year-old girl had (with a certain degree of confusion) heard of the Adam and Eve narrative in Genesis Chapters 2 and 3. Noah and the Flood are referred to in Genesis, Chapters 6 to 9; the story of Lot and his family is narrated in Genesis, Chapter 19; Chapter 16 of the Book of Judges tells of Samson and Delilah. The boy from Bethany was aware of how Moses led Israel out of Egypt and through the wilderness, as told in the Books of Exodus, Numbers and Deuteronomy. The young girl from Jericho should have listened more attentively to Chapter 10 of the Book of Joshua. She would have learned about King David's musical gifts in the First Book of Samuel 16:14-23. King Solomon's wives are to be found in the First Book of Kings 11:1-13. As for the girl from Bethlehem, she might have clarified her understanding of the Ten Commandments, in Exodus Chapter 20.

PETER ADMITS HE BELIEVES
JESUS TO BE "THE CHRIST"

JERUSALEM, 33 AD

Peter, deputy to Jesus, has confirmed he believes the preacher is "the Christ, the son of the living God". He agreed he had said this to Jesus and other members of the core campaign team at a meeting in Caesarea Philippi recently.

Peter's reluctance to say so openly since was, he explained, due to the fact that Jesus had asked the campaign group not to tell anyone he was the Christ. He was unable to say why the Galilean carpenter placed such an injunction on his friends.

A source close to the campaign said the preacher was "obviously pleased with Simon's declaration at that meeting. He said it was revealed to Simon by God himself and that from that day on he (Simon/Peter) would be his main man. He would build his administration around him, and even Hell itself would not beat it.

"Most amazingly he said he would give Simon power to make and unmake laws which would be enforced on Earth and in Heaven," the source said, adding that this surprised all the others in the core group. "Simon—that is Peter—is not a bad sort really. A bit limited though, and not very reliable. One of nature's enthusiasts. Full of vim at the beginning of any project, then he just loses interest. Not blessed in the courage department either.

"There was that time on Lake Galilee when nothing would stop him but to walk on the water to Jesus. No sooner was he out of the boat than he was panic-stricken and wailing like a baby. And down he went. Jesus, of course, pulled him out. That's Simon, all heart and not much head. Not the sort of man I'd make my deputy. John now, there's a bright spark. Or Judas. There's a man with a head on his shoulders. Makes you wonder about Jesus."

However, Peter was among the first men Jesus chose to help him in his campaign. And among the first people it is claimed Jesus cured was Peter's mother-in-law. Indeed, Peter's house in Capernaum has become, effectively, the campaign headquarters.

There is, however, no doubt that John remains one of Jesus's closest aides. He is believed to be particularly close to Mary, Jesus's mother. Yet when John and his brother James, rather presumptuously, told Jesus they wanted one of them to be his right-hand man while the other would be at his left, he said he couldn't do it. Such positions "belonged to those for whom they have been prepared," Jesus said. Cryptic as ever.

The other ten men in the core group were very angry with James and John when they heard this. That sort of one-upmanship, or indeed two-upmanship, went against the very spirit of the group. To calm the situation Jesus told them all that, where their campaign was concerned, and unlike the way it was in Palestine and elsewhere, "whoever wants to become great among you must be your servant".

He himself did not come to be served but to serve "and to give his life as a ransom for the many," he said. Again, no one understood what he meant. It was suggested this predicted martyrdom was a ploy to gain support for a flagging campaign. It was made in the wake of the death of John ("the Baptist") when the killing of preachers didn't seem so far-fetched anymore.

Indeed Jesus has since, and more explicitly, predicted his own death. This has been scoffed at by the religious and civil authorities. "This guy overestimates his own importance," said a spokesman for the High Priest, Dr Caiaphas, in response. "Jesus! ... Who?" asked a spokesman for the Governor, Mr Pilate.

It is widely speculated that had John (and James) not so fundamentally alienated the other ten in the core campaign group, with their selfish approach to Jesus, John would now be the preacher's deputy.

Some believe this could happen yet. It did not go unnoticed that it was John and James, as well as Peter, Jesus took with him to the mountain where, as all three later claimed, God spoke to the preacher and Moses and Elijah appeared with him. It is also suspected that Mary would prefer John as Jesus's deputy. And she has considerable influence over the preacher.

Peter admits he believes Jesus to be "the Christ"
See Mt 17:1–13; Mk 9:2-13; Lk 9:28–36.

PREACHER ENTERS JERUSALEM
SITTING ON A DONKEY

JERUSALEM, 33 AD

The preacher Jesus arrived in some style in Jerusalem yesterday and, to the astonishment of religious and civil authorities, he was greeted by large and enthusiastic crowds all along his route into the city.

In what some suggested was a deliberately provocative gesture, he arrived on a donkey which had been tied to a doorway in Bethany near the Mount of Olives, just outside the city.

Both civil and religious authorities in Jerusalem have a much-commented-on penchant for pomp and ceremony and Jesus's decision to enter the city on a donkey was seen as a comment on that. It was also predicted by the prophets that this was how the Messiah would arrive in Jerusalem.

Some of his supporters threw cloaks and branches on the road in the donkey's path, in what was widely described as a triumphant entry by the preacher. What surprised most commentators was that it was believed the Jesus campaign was finished and that his popularity had reached an all-time low, not least because of the severity of some of his recent comments.

Lately, however, he has begun to attract large crowds once more, mainly of the sick and their relatives. Indeed it was claimed that on his way to Jerusalem he stopped briefly at Jericho where a blind man called Bartimaeus (son of Timaeus) was begging by the roadside.

When he heard Jesus was in the area he shouted loudly at the preacher to help him. Local people were deeply embarrassed at this effrontery and told him to shut up. But he kept shouting. Jesus heard him and called him over. He asked Bartimaeus what he wanted. "I want to see," he is reported to have replied to the preacher. Jesus told him his confidence had healed him and, it was claimed, Bartimaeus could see from that moment.

Such stories had helped revive the preacher's flagging campaign and had brought out the crowds wherever he went. Yesterday in Jerusalem was no exception. What was unusual is that some of the people chanted, "We hail him who comes in the name of God. We hail the King of Israel."

It is thought that neither the religious nor civil authorities would be pleased at this. A spokesman for King Herod would not comment last night, while Governor Pilate was away for the weekend. A spokesman for the High Priest, Dr Caiaphas, dismissed the crowd's chants as "preposterous".

Passover is next week, a bit later than usual this year, and the city will be very crowded. It is assumed he has come to muster support. He has not been in Jerusalem since the preacher John died. It was said he feared for his own safety and indeed he has talked about his own imminent death a number of times since, as if to feed the rumour that there was a plot hatched by the religious authorities to have him killed.

Such a plot has been vigorously denied by spokesmen for the Sanhedrin, the council of chief priests. Last night a source close to the council expressed disquiet at the presence of Jesus in Jerusalem at this time. "Has he come to cause trouble?" he asked. "If so we cannot stand by. With the crowds this week, the potential for public disorder is great and he has said he came to turn brother against brother."

However, and despite the many miracles the Jesus campaign claims the preacher has performed, most of Jerusalem's populace remained unmoved by his arrival yesterday. But a spokesman for Dr Caiaphas expressed concern at the number of "highly respected people who have fallen for this charlatan. Some of the most unlikely Pharisees still have an open mind about this fellow. Indeed, if they were not so afraid of the justifiable ridicule that would be their lot, I do not doubt they would be more open about this."

As if to flush such people out, Jesus said last night, "when someone believes in me he does not believe in me but in the one who sent me. I am here as a light so no one who believes in me will have to stay in the dark. But I do not judge the person who does not do what I say. Judging is not what I am here for. Someone else will do that. My job is to help. What I do and say is what I was told to do and say." And few understood him.

Preacher enters Jerusalem sitting on a donkey
These events are narrated in Mt 21:1–11; Mk 11:1–11; Lk 19:28–38 and Jn 12:12–19. The story of Bartimaeus is found in Lk 18:35–43. Rumours of a plot are to be found in Mt 26:1–5; Mk 14:1–2.

BODY IS MISSING
AFTER PREACHER IS CRUCIFIED

JERUSALEM, 33 AD

By any standards it has been a remarkable week in Jerusalem. The Jesus campaign is over. Finished forever, is the consensus.

The preacher is dead and his body is missing. He was crucified by the Romans on Friday at Golgotha and laid in a sepulchre nearby. Yesterday it was discovered the stone at the front of the sepulchre had been moved and the preacher's body was gone. It is believed to have been stolen by some of his supporters for burial, at Nazareth probably, the preacher's home town. Or possibly at Capernaum, where he had his campaign headquarters.

One of his main supporters and one-time spin doctor, as well as the campaign treasurer, Judas Iscariot, was found dead, hanging from a tree, on Friday also.

It is believed his death may have been suicide. Initial reports suggest such was his despair at the execution of Jesus he decided to end his own life, but this is unclear. There have been unsubstantiated rumours in the city that he may have actually played some part in the death of Jesus.

And it has been reported that Jesus's deputy, Peter, denied on oath, and on at least three different occasions, that he ever knew the preacher.

The denials took place after Jesus was arrested on Wednesday night. They were reported in the *Moon* tabloid on Thursday under the headline "No, No, No ..."

Its front page was a stark "Crucify Him". The article

beneath demanded that Jesus "be made an example of to all these fanatics that have plagued our country".

A headline in the *Palestinian Times* on the same day asked, "What has he done?"

It called for Jesus to be released immediately and for a tribunal to be set up to investigate how "this innocent man came to be arrested in the first place. Who is responsible for this travesty?" it asked, and reminded readers that it was just a short time since the Sanhedrin, the council of chief priests, had denied vehemently there was a plot against Jesus.

Such was the pace of events last week much remains unclear but it appears Jesus and his friends met for a Passover meal on Tuesday evening in the upper room of an inn in the city.

From accounts to date it was a convivial affair, apart from two incidents which have been attributed to the amount of wine drunk. Jesus had "words" with both Peter and Judas. This may be significant in the light of what has occurred since. What Jesus said to them is not known.

Later that evening the preacher was arrested by a mob, including some soldiers and servants of the Sanhedrin (the council of chief priests), in a garden on the Mount of Olives, near the city.

It is thought he and the three men with him, Peter, and the brothers John and James, were on their way to stay the night with friends in Bethany and had paused for a breather. Possibly they planned to sleep off the wine.

A passer-by recalled passing the garden some time earlier and hearing the preacher plead to the sky: "Take this cup from me"—or something like that. He seemed to be out of his mind. And from further down the garden you could hear the snores of the other fellas. They all seemed very drunk to me," he said.

When he heard the mob approaching he hid, and saw what followed from behind a large boulder. "One man kissed the preacher before he was taken away," he said. "And one of the sleepers chopped off a soldier's ear with a swipe of his sword. He was told to put it away by Jesus, and he did. To tell you the truth, I was afraid of my life and got out of there as quick as I could."

In one of its reports of the arrest the following morning the *Moon* had a headline which asked: "Has Judas come out of the closet!" It was a reference to Mr Iscariot's kissing Jesus before the arrest. For it was he who did so.

There is much confusion over the jumble of events which followed the arrest in such rapid succession but it appears Jesus was first taken before Dr Annas, a former High Priest, and then before the current High Priest, Dr Caiaphas. He was then sent to Governor Pilate who seems to have been unhappy about ordering an execution and twice asked the crowds what he should do. They demanded crucifixion, both times. And so it was done on Friday.

"The End", announced Saturday's *Moon.*

Body is missing after preacher crucified
For the events leading up to the arrest of Jesus see Mt 26:17–56; Mk 14: 10–52; Lk 22:7–53; Jn 13:1–18:12. For Peter's denials, see Mt 26:69–75; Mk 14:66–72; Lk 22:54–62; Jn 18:16–27.
See also Acts 1:15–20 and Mt 27:3–10.

Rumours sweep city
as preacher's body still missing

Jerusalem, 33 AD

Sensational rumours have been sweeping the city as the body of Jesus, the preacher executed for blasphemy last Friday week, remained missing. The religious authorities have had a difficult time explaining how the body, which was guarded round-the-clock by their own soldiers, could have been taken.

It is still believed members of the Jesus campaign stole the remains, intending burial in Galilee. However, despite intensive investigations there, especially in Nazareth and Capernaum, there has been no evidence to date of any such burial. The investigations continue.

Indeed, though keeping a very low profile since the execution and still in some disarray, most members of the Jesus campaign are still in Jerusalem, including the preacher's mother Mary, her sister, and his close friend John.

Fanciful suggestions that Jesus has risen from the dead have been dismissed as "a joke" by a spokesman for the High Priest, Dr Caiaphas. "Is that a serious question?" he asked, adding that "of course there are people who will not accept he is dead. It happens all the time. There are people out there who still believe King David is alive and well, all these centuries later."

But as the week progressed reports that Jesus had been seen multiplied. An inn-keeper from Emmaus said the preacher had a meal there during the week with two of his friends. One of Jesus's closest friends, Mary of Magdala, said she saw him on the Sunday morning after the execution. She had gone to visit his tomb and found it empty. She began to weep, when the gardener spoke to her. "It was Jesus," she said.

It was also reported that Jesus visited his followers that night in a room in the city where they had locked themselves in, for their own safety. All the rumours remained unsubstantiated and were not taken seriously until Thursday's *Palestinian Times* reported "Soldier Claims Jesus Alive".

It quoted one of the soldiers who had been guarding the preacher's grave as saying he had seen Jesus alive. "The earth shook and this guy, wearing very bright shiny clothes, appeared out of nowhere and rolled back the stone in front of the tomb. There were two women from the Jesus campaign there and the man told them Jesus had risen. He showed them the empty grave and said Jesus was in Galilee and would meet them there. As the women left another man spoke to them and one of the women recognised him and became very emotional. He told them to go to Galilee as well. I saw him myself. He was the spit of Jesus."

At a hastily arranged press conference Dr Caiaphas denied emphatically there was any truth to the story. The soldier quoted in the newspaper was, he said, "unwell, and has been for years. You will find none of his colleagues saw any of these things." Three soldiers at the press conference with him confirmed what he said.

He was dismissive of the reports of sightings of Jesus. "Emmaus has had a bad season. They could do with a bit of business there," he said, "and as for Mary of Magdala, well how can anyone take the word of that woman seriously." This was a reference to rumours about Mary's past, rumours which have been vigorously denied by her friends. Dr Caiaphas insisted, however, that they were true.

Rumours sweep city as preacher's body still missing
For these extraordinary events, look at Mt 27:57–28:10;
Mk 16:1–20; Lk 23:50–24:35; Jn 19:38–21:25.

REPORT ABSOLVES RELIGIOUS LEADERS
OVER THE EXECUTION OF PREACHER

JERUSALEM, 33 AD

A report published this week found that events leading to the recent execution of Jesus had been handled "in an exemplary fashion" by the religious authorities here. "It is clear everything that could be done was done, to avoid this unfortunate man's death," it concluded. It said opinion had been sought from other jurisdictions as to how the situation might have been handled by their religious authorities. "Everywhere it was the same. All praised the restraint shown by the religious leadership in Jerusalem and their unwavering insistence on due process being followed throughout these sad events," it said.

The report had been prepared by the High Priest's office, "following concerns expressed at events leading to the preacher's execution," as it was put in a preamble. It continued that "the High Priest, Dr Caiaphas, personally appointed three of his most senior officials to conduct the investigation which led to this report. He advised them to stop at nothing to get truthful answers to the queries raised since the crucifixion," it said.

At a press conference to launch the report a spokesman for Dr Caiaphas said the High Priest "was most anxious to ensure no stone was unturned in establishing the truth of what had taken place and had instructed his officials accordingly."

The spokesman strongly disagreed with a reporter who

suggested that the report may have been prepared because of anger at Governor Pilate's office over the execution. "Nothing could be further from the truth. After all, if it wasn't for Governor Pilate the crucifixion could not have taken place. You must remember the religious authorities in this city do not have powers to carry out executions. Only the Romans can do that. And it was they who crucified Jesus," he said.

Explaining the High Priest's absence from the press conference, he said Dr Caiaphas was ill. He sent his apologies. It is known the High Priest suffers from a recurring stomach complaint which has prevented him attending other press conferences in the past. The report said the events leading to Jesus's death began with Judas Iscariot, treasurer of the Jesus campaign. "Mr Iscariot came to the High Priest's office accompanied by officers of the Temple guard. He appeared agitated and said Jesus was planning a coup against the religious authorities.

"He was also disturbed by claims made by the preacher that he was 'the Son of God'; that he was the Messiah foretold by the prophets. He questioned Jesus's sanity and advised that something must be done or there would be riots in the city by the weekend. He predicted chaos and many deaths. It was known Mr Iscariot was one of the most influential members of the Jesus campaign. Besides, it had already been reported to the High Priest's office that Jesus had been inciting the crowds against the religious leadership. He had described them as 'blind guides', 'hypocrites', 'snakes', a 'brood of vipers'.

"Just that week, he said members of the religious

leadership liked to go around in flowing robes and to be greeted on the streets as the high and mighty. He said they had the most important seats in the synagogues and at banquets. 'They devour widows' houses and for a show make lengthy prayers,' he had said.

"It was agreed Jesus should be arrested in the interest of public order and safety," the report said. "Unfortunately, Mr Iscariot refused to lead our officers to where Jesus would be, unless he was paid. A sum of 30 pieces of silver was agreed. He led our soldiers to a garden, where Jesus was arrested.

"The preacher was brought before the High Priest, the chief priests, elders and teachers of the law. At a formal hearing witnesses repeated what Jesus had said. He denied nothing. It was felt then he should be handed over to the Romans so he could be dealt with in strict compliance with the law."

The High Priest's office regretted that the situation had arisen. "We were confronted with a circumstance that was potentially too serious to be ignored. Lives were at risk. Our sympathy goes to the deceased's family," it said.

Report absolves religious leaders
See Mk 14:53–65; Lk 23:1–11; Jn 18:13–19:16.

LEAKED ROMAN LETTER CAUSES UPROAR

JERUSALEM, 33 AD

There was consternation in the city this week following a letter written in Governor Pilate's office which was leaked to the *Palestinian Times*. The letter was fiercely critical of the city's religious authorities. It described them as "venal", "probably corrupt", "deceitful", and as "those awful people".

A spokesman for the High Priest, Dr Caiaphas, said he would not be commenting on the letter until its status had been established. In a hastily released statement, a spokesman for the Governor said the letter has been written by a junior in the Governor's office. It had been intended for a friend of the official's in Rome. The official "vehemently denied leaking it to the media and has since returned to Rome," it said.

The letter complained about the "dullness" of the Jerusalem posting. "This place is really small grapes in the scheme of things," it said. "Nothing much happens. Ever. Last week's highlight, for instance, was the crucifixion of a peasant from a kip called Nazareth.

"You really would not want to go there, believe me. This fellow claimed to be God—they believe there is just one of those in these parts (no imagination)—and the local holy Joes lost it.

"They leant on the Guv to have him killed and, well you know old Ponti. He's just a guy who can't say no! So this peasant—probably just a bit dotty—was crucified on Friday. Which is a pity, as he was not a bad looking guy. And there are not too many of those in these parts."

The letter explained that the High Priest, Dr Caiaphas, and the chief priests had arrived at the Governor's palace the previous Thursday morning "with this pleasant peasant who had his hands tied behind his back. They were slavering for blood. Still they would not come into the palace as they consider us unclean!

"And you should see them. As venal, corrupt, and deceitful a gang as it has been my displeasure to ever come across. 'Those awful people' is how we refer to them in the office. The Guv went out to meet them. Any other man would have told them where to go! He asked what charges there were against the peasant and they said: 'If he wasn't a criminal we wouldn't be handing him to you.'

"He saw through them immediately. They wanted this guy killed because somehow they felt threatened by him. And he looked as innocent as a lamb. Gorgeous!

"They had tried this sort of thing before. And Caiaphas, their boss—as crafty and crooked an old fox as I've ever come across—had been quoted as saying that it was better this peasant should die than all his people be put at risk. Presumably from us. As if we cared. These people have such an inflated view of themselves!

"Anyhow, the Guv told them 'go to hell' in diplomatic language. But—you won't believe this—they pleaded, 'But we can't execute him'! As usual they wanted us to do their dirty work for them. How ... unclean!

"The Guv really didn't need another row with those religious nuts so he brought the peasant into the palace for questioning.

"And there was this bizarre discussion about 'what is a king?' The peasant said he was a king and his kingdom 'was not of this world'. And I am Caesar. Out of this world, baby! 'Everyone on the side of truth listens to me.' the peasant said. 'What is truth?' asked Ponti and I thought 'oh no, there goes the day'. You know how the Guv loves these sort of discussions.

"But he went back to the 'holy' men outside and said he could find nothing to charge the preacher with. And they got mad and asked for Barabbas in exchange for the preacher.

"Now, Barabbas is an animal. He killed many innocent people during a rebellion. And this was the man these nuts wanted exchanged for a preacher! It is a custom here to release a prisoner at the Passover feast, which took place last week.

"So Barabbas was released and the peasant was flogged, with Ponti hoping that would satisfy the priests. But it didn't. Then he washed his hands and said 'upon your heads be it' and the peasant was brought off for crucifixion and just to annoy the priests the Guv put the sign 'Jesus (the preacher's name) of Nazareth King of the Jews' over the top of the cross. It drove them crazy."

Leaked Roman letter causes uproar
For the trial and death of Jesus, see Mt 26:57–27:56; Mk 15:1–47; Lk 22:54–23:49; Jn 18:13–19:37.

Rumours persist
that preacher seen alive

Jerusalem, 33 AD

Rumours that the preacher Jesus, who was crucified in Jerusalem some weeks ago, has since been seen alive continue to persist.

A spokesman for the High Priest, Dr Caiaphas, said his office had been "driven to distraction" by queries from people inquiring whether the preacher was really dead at all. "He is dead, dead, dead," he said.

The rumours have been fuelled by the continued absence of the body. Investigations have so far failed to locate the preacher's grave/sepulchre or indeed any unacknowledged newly dug ground or newly-occupied sepulchre in the whole of Galilee.

"We must accept that the body of Jesus has been buried in some secret location, possibly the desert," said the High Priest's spokesman. He also said that the village of Bethany had been searched, but to no avail. It is where Jesus's close friends Lazarus, Mary, and Martha live.

"For reasons that are not yet clear it appears members of the 'Jesus Campaign' have hidden the body," said the spokesman.

This has been vigorously denied by members of the campaign. Jesus's deputy Simon, now known as Peter, said he had himself met Jesus since he was crucified. "In fact we have met him three times since the crucifixion," said Peter.

"On the day his body was reported missing he visited

us in Jerusalem. A week later he did so again. That time Thomas put his fingers where the nails had been in his hands and where he had been pierced in the side," he said. Thomas corroborated this.

"And we met him again on the shores of Lake Galilee. We—myself, Thomas, Nathanael, James and John—were fishing there when we saw him on the shore. He called out to us to fish on the right side of the boat. When we did we weren't able to haul in the net. There were 153 fish in it and still it didn't break. He told us bring some fish with us when we went to him. He had set a fire and was cooking on it. He also had bread for us. 'Come on, have breakfast,' he said," recalled Peter, "and we did."

His recollections were corroborated by Thomas, Nathanael, John, and James, all members of the Jesus Campaign team. They also said Jesus reinstated Peter as his lieutenant. This surprised them, they claimed, as Peter had denied ever knowing Jesus after the preacher was arrested and prior to his crucifixion.

"This is all simply ludicrous," said the High Priest's spokesman. "Is it not peculiar that the only people who claim to have seen Jesus since he was executed and—hardly coincidental—since his body went missing, are all members of the Jesus Campaign?" he asked.

"It seems clear to me these people wish to persist in deluding innocent people and to continue where Jesus left off with their simplistic explanations, their suspect 'miracles', and their crude blasphemies. They should realise we cannot allow this sort of thing to continue. Simon, Peter, or whatever he calls himself now, must think we are all fools. This is a man who abandoned and denied he knew Jesus. Three times! What credibility can he have?

"It's all so fantastic it would be hilarious if it weren't for the fact that there are people who might well believe this nonsense. Jesus is dead. He is still dead, and he will remain dead. Is it not somewhat unlikely that an uneducated carpenter's son from Nazareth would be the first man in history to rise from the dead? But of course he himself tried to get away with similar claims.

"It was said he raised the daughter of a rabbi from the dead and, most notoriously of all, there was the case of his friend Lazarus. People should have a bit of sense and recognise all this nonsense for what it is—a bid for power. Towards what end we know not," he said.

Rumours persist that preacher seen alive
See Mt 28:16–20; Mk 16:1–20; Lk 24: 36–53; Jn 20:19–21:25.

TABLOID SLAMS THE "NO CANDIDATE" CAMPAIGN

JERUSALEM, 33 AD

The Jesus Campaign has resumed, without Jesus! Or, as the *Moon* tabloid dubbed it last week, "the No Candidate Campaign".

In a hard-hitting article it said: "So Peter—or should that be Simon?—has *resurrected* [the newspaper's italics] the 'Jesus Campaign'.

"Is that the same Simon—or should that be Peter?—who so recently denied he ever, ever, ever knew Jesus, though he was his deputy? Then he was speaking in the shadow of Golgotha, and courage was never ever, ever, ever Peter's—or should that be Simon's?—strength.

"He and his buddies stole Jesus's body, hid it no one knows where, and now they tell us the preacher is alive and well and probably has appeared at a village near you. And he expects to be believed. A hell of an assumption!

"Or should that be ascension? 'Oh, he ascended into Heaven,' he said when asked where Jesus was now. So convenient. Especially as (to date) no one gives interviews from Heaven. It is time this joker and his fellow clowns were dealt with. They have learned nothing from the crucifixion of their ne'er-do-well leader. Maybe it's time they got the same treatment?"

The core group of the movement formerly known as the "Jesus Campaign" gathered for a meeting in the city yesterday and, following what was said to be a rowdy get-together, they decided to pick up where they left off when

Jesus was crucified.

They also replaced Judas Iscariot. He was paid to lead the High Priest's soldiers to Gethsemane where the preacher was found. Following the arrest he was overcome by guilt. It is claimed he hanged himself.

His replacement is Matthias, about whom little is known. Another candidate for the vacancy was "the man of three names"—Joseph, also called Barsabbas and Justus. The group used lots to pick him. It is a favoured method of election, as it avoids the embarrassment of a count and ensures full support for the winner.

As well as the 11 surviving members of the core campaign group, yesterday's meeting was attended by the usual retinue of women who played such a role in the Jesus Campaign, as well as the preacher's mother, Mary, and his brothers.

Leaving the meeting in high spirits, a reinvigorated group went into the streets of Jerusalem talking a bewildering range of babble. Some foreigners claimed to understand what they said, but the local consensus was that the group had been up all night carousing and was very drunk.

People who had been staying near where the group had met recalled there had been a lot of noise. "It was like trying to sleep through a thunder-storm," said one local resident.

On hearing that members of the group had claimed that flames, like tongues, had appeared over the heads of everyone at the gathering, another resident wondered, "What were they on?" He said he had drunk all sorts of wine in his day but he had never seen anything like that.

Peter denied they had any drink taken. "It's only nine in the morning," he said, and quoted from the prophet Joel: "... Your young men will see visions and your old men will dream dreams ..." He said Jesus had conquered death. That he had been sent by God, as King David had forecast, and that he was the Messiah.

Some believed him and asked what they should do. "Be sorry for your sins and be baptised," he said. An estimated 3,000 people did so. It was also claimed that he cured a beggar who had been crippled from birth.

Sources in the city last night indicated that the council of chief priests intended wasting no time in acting against the Peter group.

Tabloid slams the "no candidate" campaign
For Peter's new-found confidence and that of the early church, see Acts 1:1–26 and Acts 2:1–36.

KIND YOUNG MAN STONED BY MOB

JERUSALEM, 33 AD

His name was Stephen and all agreed he was a very kind young man. He was stoned to death by a mob on Tuesday.

As he fell, when a rock hit him on the head, he prayed: "Do not hold this against them." Minutes later he was dead.

The *Palestinian Times* asked on Wednesday: "What is becoming of our country? An inoffensive young man is murdered because of nothing other than his strange beliefs. Who among us is safe?"

However, the *Moon* tabloid, on its front page, announced: "Where Lies Lead …", over a report on the killing of Stephen. "He denigrated our people. He blamed us for Abraham's problems. He blamed us for Moses's problems. He blamed us for the death of that vagabond Jesus who, outrageously, he said was the son of God. 'We have always persecuted prophets,' he said. He got what he deserved."

The *Palestinian Times* demanded the Roman authorities intervene and "bring civility back to our city. It is clear our religious authorities, in particular, either have lost control of or do not wish to exercise control over elements who have murder in mind." It referred to the recent crucifixion of the preacher Jesus "in circumstances where due process was demonstrably not adhered to", and called for an independent investigation into both it and "the killing of Stephen".

A spokesman for the High Priest, Dr Caiaphas, dismissed this as "typical of the anti-religious stance of that newspaper". He pointed to the investigation into Jesus's death "which exonerated this office totally".

He said a similar investigation was under way into the death of Stephen and added that "if some find these investigations unsatisfactory we will not stand in the way of an inquiry conducted by people outside the Sanhedrin (the Council of Chief Priests)."

Stephen had recently become associated with the Peter group, which was formed some time after the death of the preacher Jesus.

He was one of seven young men chosen to help the group with its campaign, and which had met with unexpected success in convincing the people Jesus was the Messiah.

He outraged the Sanhedrin, however, when he was brought before it, by asserting that they had murdered the son of God and those sent before him. "God-murderers, that's what he called us," said one outraged chief priest, before Stephen was set upon in a most unruly scene.

The Sanhedrin had previously brought Peter and his friend John before it. They commanded them to stop saying Jesus was the Messiah. Sources say they were surprised at the courage of two such "simple, uneducated men", as one source put it. "But it would be more in their line to be back in Capernaum controlling their children," he said.

Peter and his group, however, continued as before, convincing as many as 5,000, (some claimed) of what they said. Peter himself seemed to have acquired the charisma of Jesus where crowds were concerned. They believed he too could perform miracles.

On the instruction of the religious authorities, Peter and members of the group were arrested and jailed but, astonishingly, they escaped.

They were arrested again and brought before the Sanhedrin where a respected man, called Gamaliel, advised that they be left alone. He recalled similar groups in the past, of whom nothing had been heard since. He said: "Leave them to God. If there's any truth in whay they say there's no use fighting them. If there's not, they'll just disappear." It was agreed the group should be flogged and let go.

They then resumed their campaign. That was when they were joined by Stephen.

Kind young man stoned by mob
See Acts 6:1-15 and 7:1–60 as well as Acts 4:1–22 and 5:12–21.
The wise Gamaliel is referred to in Acts 5:22–42.
For Saul see Acts 8:1–3.

Saul of Tarsus
hunts down Peter's lying sect

Jerusalem, 33 AD

Saul, one of the city's rising stars, has been accused by the
Peter group of being their "chief persecutor". They claimed he
was present at the stoning of Stephen, and that he encouraged
the killing.

The *Moon* tabloid first used the "chief persecutor" label.
A spokesman for the High Priest's office dismissed the
allegations as "typical fabrication", and was dismissive of the
Moon.

"Like the celestial body after which it is named, stories
in that paper tend to be a pale reflection of the truth," he said.

Saul was "one of the great defenders of the faith. He has
persecuted no one. But he has saved many from the lies of
Peter and his sect, as well as helping bring them to justice.
That is not persecution. That is upholding the law," he said.

Saul is deeply committed to Judaism and takes pride in
"doing God's work", as he has described his efforts to curb the
Peter group. "These cults have to be stopped before they get
out of control. Already thousands of our people have been
misled. Every day I have parents coming to me saying their
children have abandoned the family to live like vagabonds,
deceived by the fantasies of that carpenter from Nazareth," he
said.

When it was pointed out that he was himself a tent
maker, and from Tarsus, Saul responded: "I have behind me
millennia of tradition and all the wisdom and authority that

goes with that. What have these yokels behind them but ignorance and the daft notions of a Nazarene with delusions of grandeur?"

He made no apology for trying to save his people from "such mythology", he said, and drew attention to "the type of people involved in this carry-on". He spoke of Peter's "well-known weakness of character. He abandoned his family to follow Jesus, and lies with great ease. Matthew robbed his own people for the Romans. James and John left their elderly father on his own in Capernaum. And Judas Iscariot sold the lot of them for a few coins, before hanging himself!

"These then are the men who expect us to believe Jesus was the Messiah and they are his chosen followers. Their beliefs are nothing more than a hotch-potch of foreign ideas, grafted on to a few fantasies, with a smattering of Judaism in the background. That Jesus rose from the dead and ascended to heaven is lifted straight from the Persian Zoroastrian religion, for instance," he said.

It was a peculiar feature of the Peter group that it favoured foreign ideas and notions so much. Saul went on. "Look at the name Peter, for example - it's Greek! 'Simon' was a perfectly good Jewish name but it was not good enough for the Nazarene. No man should change his name. It's what was given him.

"And look at how many women follow them around. Look at their long hair and uncovered heads. They are a thorn in the side of men who want to live decently. Next thing they'll be teaching the same lies as the men do. Do they not know God created Adam first, then Eve? That Adam wasn't the one deceived by the serpent? It was the woman. Woman was the first sinner. How quickly they have forgotten the truth," he said.

In Jerusalem the crisis provoked by the Peter group appears to be under control. Some members remain in the city but are keeping a low profile. Others have established themselves in Samaria where one of the group leaders, Philip, has made a big impact.

There were also reports from as far north as Damascus that the group was making inroads there. Hearing this, Saul requested letters from the High Priest for synagogues in Damascus so that Peter's followers there could be jailed. He left for Damascus last night "still breathing out murderous threats" against the Peter group, as one source put it. He is due back within days.

Saul of Tarsus hunts down Peter's lying sect
For Saul's efforts against the early church, see Acts 8:1–3.
The work of Philip is in Acts 8:4–40 and Paul's setting out for Damascus is referred to in Acts 9:1–2. At to what happened next, look at Acts 9:3–30!

REFERENCES

The Jesus Reports were first published in *The Irish Times* on Mondays during the year 2000.